MANAGING FOR HEALTH RESULT

Papers from a King's Fund International Seminar

MANAGING FOR HEALTH RESULT

Papers from a King's Fund International Seminar

edited by Nan Carle

King Edward's Hospital Fund for London

Typeset by DP Press, St Julians, Sevenoaks, England
Printed and bound in England by Hollen Street Press

Distributed for the King's Fund by Bailey Distribution Ltd

ISBN 1 85551 060 X

King's Fund Publishing Office
14 Palace Court
London W2 4HT

CONTENTS

LIST OF CONTRIBUTORS

Nan Carle   Fellow, King's Fund College

Cyril Chantler   Chairman, Management Board, Guy's Acute Unit, Guy's Hospital (now Clinical Dean, United Medical and Dental Schools of Guy's and St Thomas's Hospitals)

Glenn Garlick   Chief Executive, Waikato Hospital Board, Hamilton (now General Manager, Waitkato Area Health Board)

Robert Johnson   Chief Executive Officer, St Louis Regional Medical Center (now Executive Director, Grady Memorial Hospital, Atlanta)

Brendon Kearney   Administrator, Royal Adelaide Hospital

Dieter Kuntz   Executive Director, Victoria General Hospital, Winnipeg

Alasdair Liddell   District General Manager, Bloomsbury Health Authority (now Chief Executive, East Anglian Regional Health Authority)

Robert J Maxwell Secretary and Chief Executive Officer, King Edward's Hospital Fund for London

John Morris   Executive Director, Australian Hospital Association (now Chief Executive Officer, Peter MacCallum Cancer Institute, Melbourne)

Scott S Parker   President, Intermountain Health Care Incorporated, Salt Lake City

George Salmond   Director-General, Department of Health, Wellington

Cameron Waddell Manager, Occupational Health, Petro-Canada Incorporated, Calgary

ACKNOWLEDGMENTS

Many of the arguments and debates in this book have been raging since at least the time of Hippocrates. The experiences of these managers, however, are fresh in their search for solutions and for support to manage with vision. In the attempt to present their ideas in a framework of adaptive change I am deeply grateful to Ann Shearer for her professional guidance in helping to edit the papers, to Gordon Best for his timeless supply of good ideas and to Robert Maxwell for not letting me say no.

We are also grateful to the Kellogg Foundation for its support of the 1988 King's Fund International Seminar, for which the papers contained here were originally written, and for contributing to the costs of producing this book.

The contributors also wish to thank the people that supported them in writing their papers. Deiter Kuntz particularly requested that Alice Jope and Claudia Bridges received mention for reviewing and preparing his manuscripts.

PREFACE

WHAT IS HEALTH RESULT?

Robert Maxwell

The basic idea is obvious enough. We ought to be able to state what effect an intervention aimed at improving health is intended to achieve, and then see whether it does. In practice, however, things are not that simple.

The consequential links between intervention and result frequently contain elements of uncertainty. Many therapies in common use, and widely believed to have good effect, have never been rigorously evaluated. The gold standard for evaluation is the randomised controlled trial (RCT)[1], yet most therapies have not been subject to an RCT, sometimes for good reason. When this has been done, the results are frequently ambiguous, with subsidiary questions unanswered and conclusions in terms of mathematical probabilities, not certainties. In addition, it may take a considerable time before outcome can be defined with any certainty: cancer, for example, is often assessed in terms of survival at five years after intervention. Moreover, few fields of human knowledge change as fast as biological science, so that today's RCT results, however scrupulously collected and analysed, could represent yesterday's truth.

There is the fact, too, that health care, however good, is not the same thing as health. What matters has to be health. The patient may survive and prosper despite poor health care. Equally, the most meticulous care may not produce a good result in any one case. Of course many illnesses will clear up quickly with appropriate treatment, or even without it, but many others will not, particularly when the illness is complex and chronic.

Health is in any case relative, depending upon the age, attributes, behaviour and luck of each individual. In this sense the World Health Organization definition of positive 'wellness' is dangerously misleading.[2] The vigour, well-being and virtual unconsciousness of physical limitations that may be assumed as a right by many young people are irrelevant for anyone with a serious, long-term disability, including most older people. Health is limited to a greater or lesser extent for anyone who is not currently an Olympic athlete in a perfect state of physical and mental well-being, and no amount of health care will magically produce or maintain that ideal.

Even death, the most apparently unambiguous measure of failure of health care, has its own ambiguities. For one thing, it is ultimately inescapable. For another, many therapies may involve pain, indignity and other disadvantages which unacceptably outweigh any benefit they may bring in extending life. In this sense, all health care needs to recognise the ultimate inevitability of failure.

To restate the argument so far:

Much health care, well intentioned, rests on assumptions about results that fall well short of certainties.

Even when the evidence about results is strong, it may be out of date because medical knowledge continues to develop quickly.

Health care is a means to an end (health), not an end in itself. But health depends on many variables besides health care, and is relative rather than absolute.

The law of diminishing returns applies in health care. Even small, expensive gains may well be worth having, but they are not necessarily worth the cost in terms of money or of pain.

Health failure may in some cases be easier to measure than health success. No health success is permanent, because the only certainties in human life are about ageing and, ultimately, death.

Facets and levels

Good health care which is relevant to, but not a guarantee of, good health, has more than one dimension. Elsewhere[3] I have postulated the six dimensions of health care quality which are:

access to services
relevance to needs (for the whole community)
effectiveness (for individual patients)
equity (fairness)
social acceptability
efficiency and economy

The most important point, however, is not whether these six are definitive, but that the matter is complex and multidimensional. A technical definition of quality in the treatment of the individual patient tends to be uppermost in the minds of the responsible professionals, for instance. But patient satisfaction is also important, and this depends on being treated with respect and the perception of an acceptable result. In grading the performance of a whole system, questions of equity, relevance and economy are as important as the skill and humanity received by the individual patient. If some people do not have access to adequate care, or receive much poorer care than others – as is patently the case in the United States and in much of South America – the system as a whole is under-performing. If important, soluble health problems are ignored, while attention is lavished on others that are relatively trivial or intractable, or even both, then the system is failing to deliver quality.

Different people are obviously needed to make reliable judgments about these different dimensions of quality. Technical performance can generally be judged only by the relevant technical experts. But the patient's own voice has to be paramount in assessments of patient satisfaction. And judgments about relevance, equity and economy need to draw on epidemiological skills and the social sciences as much as on clinical expertise.

Any adequate discussion of the multifaceted nature of quality must recognise not only different points of view, but also different levels of assessment. In the Hippocratic tradition, the welfare of the individual patient is paramount for the physician, and the fiduciary relationship is between these two, without equivocation or excuse. That should properly remain the case today, even though the physician is likely to be part of a complex team. But there are also other important levels at which to assess health result. To take the extreme: a whole nation's health can be relatively good or bad, as can the performance of its entire health system. Of course the nation is made up of people, so that aggregate measurement of health result is in a sense simply the sum of all the results for individuals. The aggregate will, however, include those who have failed to obtain appropriate care and subsume the statistical variations inherent in the pattern of individual outcomes, while making it even more difficult to assess causal relationships. Improvements in medical care have certainly played a part in the phenomenal improvement in Japan's health results during the last 20 years. But it would be naive for any other nation to mimic the Byzantine complexities of the Japanese health care system and expect to achieve the same remarkable results, which are at least equally dependent on diet, social patterns, sustained economic advance, and relatively abstemious habits.

The extremes of health result, then, have to do with medical care and its impact on health for the individual and for the nation. There are also relevant levels in between: the family or the household, for example, or the local community, or a discrete social or demographic subgroup. For instance, alternative patterns of individual care may make very different demands on family, partners and friends, as well as on the patient, and their viewpoints will not always be identical. Different ethnic groups may have different expectations about health behaviour and appropriate professional care, and they may well also have different experiences of how the system actually performs. At times Julian Tudor Hart's 'inverse care law' undoubtedly applies: those in greatest need find the system at its worst.[4]

The measurement of health result does not necessarily become more complicated at the higher levels between individual and nation. Cause and effect probably do become harder to pinpoint; it becomes harder to say that a particular therapeutic intervention has had a particular result for the population at large. But the problems of statistical variation tend to eliminate themselves, and the time lag may be less of a problem in identifying trends. So, for example, we can be far more confident at the national level than the individual about the benefits from reduced cigarette smoking, changes in diet, or average alcohol consumptions, and collective alterations in behaviour can begin to show themselves quite fast. National patterns of food and alcohol distribution and purchasing, or of cigarette sales, can be monitored monthly, or even weekly, on the basis of seasonal moving averages, giving far more rapid feedback of information than is generally feasible at individual level.

Principles and building blocks

No nation yet does anything like an adequate job of measuring health result, and there is even a shortage of clear conceptual models. There are nevertheless examples, including a number in this book, of attempts to link activities to assessed needs and to measure impact (see Figure 1.1). Examples may be fragmentary and incomplete, but that does not lessen their importance, and some worthwhile pointers can be drawn from them.

Figure 1.1

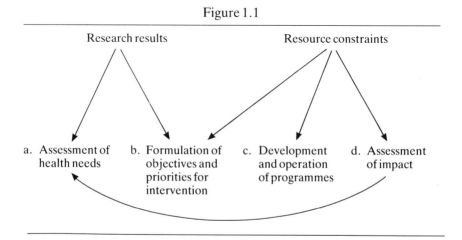

a. Assessment of health needs

b. Formulation of objectives and priorities for intervention

c. Development and operation of programmes

d. Assessment of impact

Research results   Resource constraints

14

1. *Health results are best formulated and assessed for a defined, reference population*

It is extremely helpful to know what specific population any agency or programme seeks to serve. The definition can be geographic (everyone within a particular area), in terms of subscribers (as with an HMO or an insurance agency) or related to employment.

Without a clear, comprehensive definition we are almost bound to overlook important needs and lack a reliable database to measure impact. To take a simple example: around 1920 the major teaching hospital in Cali, Colombia, was running a sophisticated neonatal programme with survival comparable to the results achieved in the leading US centres at that time. Almost by accident, the people running the programme discovered with horror that their long-term results were quite different: 70 per cent of those whom they discharged home successfully were dead within three months – because of poverty, poor nutrition and infectious disease.[5] While such disastrous outcomes should arguably be identified by follow-up studies, the existence of a reliable comprehensive database provides a necessary, independent check to avoid self-delusion. It is only too easy to assume that interventions are as successful as their promoters hope. An independent database keeps us honest.

The less selective the defined population, the better it will be. A subscriber or employment related scheme, for instance, will very likely omit some of those in greatest need. That may not be a problem for the agency; but it is for those who are left out and, hence, also in terms of overall local or national result. Brendon Kearney's chapter in this book gives an impressive example of an attempt to link state-wide data on cancer prevalence and survival rates with institutional data on programmes, priorities and choices.

2. *Health results should be specified in terms of tangible health benefits*

Medicine is, among other things, a science and it is perfectly legitimate for research purposes to assess results in terms of knowledge gained. Business organisations in the health field will assess results in ways that include such standard yardsticks as profitability and return on investment. Health is also so important in terms of public policy and public expenditure that governments will have explicit or implicit political objectives. What should be paramount, however, despite these many legitimate and disparate interests, is the health benefit to individuals and/or to the collective community. This is not to claim the individual's own assessment of quality and result as the sole authority. Patients should be the principal judges of the manner of care and of their own satisfaction with outcome, but they are not able to assess technical quality. It is to claim, however, that the pre-eminent question in judging health result is *whose health benefits, and to what extent?* This applies as strongly at the collective level as at the individual. So clinicians need to think far more broadly than the Hippocratic oath suggests. They need to consider not just individual patients but the impact of what they do on the community's health and the application of the resources that they command.

3. *Health results should always take account of other relevant policies, services and influences*

Health result frequently depends on a wide range of factors – conventional health services is only one of them. It is stupid, as well as arrogant, to ignore these other influences. There is no way in which a single service or agency can do everything that needs to be done; nor can it operate effectively, with limited resources, without taking note of what others can contribute, whether these are health or other services, public or private.

4. *Formulating and assessing health result is an inherent professional responsibility*

Health result can only be measured with the active support and involvement of the health care professions acting on the patient's behalf, with corresponding personal and collective accountability. It is an integral part of their responsibility to assess results rigorously in terms of patient benefit and, in view of the powers of modern medicine to do harm as well as good, the vulnerability and trust of those who seek their professional help, and the scale of resources at their command.

5. *Different aspects of health care need different definitions and measurements of results*

Prevention, cure and care ought to be complementary rather than in conflict.[6] They do, however, call for a flexible and catholic approach to assessment. Most discussion of medical audit has been in the context of acute care, especially surgery. Assessing health result in the context of chronic illness or handicap is very different: maximising choice, autonomy, dignity and independence becomes more important, and complete technical success less so. Differences between one kind of health care result and another may generally be a matter of degree: dignity and choice also matter in acute care, and technical improvement also has its place in chronic care. Nevertheless it is vital to recognise, first, that working towards definable health result is not just of relevance to curative medicine and, second, that some ideas and techniques of assessment are bound to be different in the fields of long-term care and of prevention.

6. In assessing health result, the fundamental criterion is outcome

Donabedian's differentiation between structure, process and outcome is operationally useful, provided that everyone recognises the first two as means not ends and that the fundamental criterion is outcome. Because of the common delay between intervention and end result, proxy measure are important. So it can be useful to specify the ('structural') characteristics of a properly equipped and staffed transplant or dialysis unit, or the ('process') requirements for a high standard of diagnosis or treatment. Equally, however, we must be prepared continually to question and revise these requirements because some are based on unsound assumptions and others are superseded by medical change. Structural and process yardsticks can be useful operational guidelines, so long as they are frequently reconsidered and are anchored in reliable evidence about their effect on outcome.

Implications

1. While these are genuine difficulties about measuring impact, these difficulties ought not to be used as an excuse. Much more effort has to go into assessing health result because:

without that we have no 'bottom line' beyond the financial;

large sums of money are being spent in the health system and these should be matched by accountability;

hard choices are inescapable and these ought to be based on some systematic assessment of the consequences of the choices made.

2. However each system is organised, somebody ought to be looking at overall consequences. This must be government, if only by default, which should be assessing how the system actually works and striving for changes to make it work acceptably. (This is not an argument for government to run the system, but to assess its overall effectiveness.)

3. Important as money is, the greatest difficulties are less about finance than about clarifying objectives and keeping expectations realistic.

17

4. Both the public and the private sectors have to change radically in terms of articulating their mission and strategy, their values, style and way they do business. For example:

government agencies need to be more businesslike;

autonomous institutions and agencies should be much clearer about the ultimate value of what they are doing and how that fits into the broader pattern of provision in achieving health result;

politicians should concentrate on defining mission and strategy, and the bargain that they want to strike with providers. They must not get involved in the detail of how institutions manage to fulfill their side of the bargain.

5. Running the health care system effectively and efficiently is a big enough challenge by any standards. However, it is also sensible in any community to approach the problem from the other end: how can maximum health gains be made? This will suggest actions in and outside the health care system. The task needs to be approached with the same attention to evidence and medical knowledge as any question about therapeutic effectiveness. It also gives a different – and sometimes salutory – perspective on the appropriateness of some of the activities of the health care system.

References

1. Cochrane, A L. Effectiveness and efficiency. Rock Carling Fellowship 1971. London, Nuffield Provincial Hospitals Trust, 1972.

2. Sagan, Leonard A. The health of nations: true causes of sickness and well-being. New York, Basic Books Inc.

3. Maxwell, R J. Perspectives in NHS management: quality assessment in health. British Medical Journal, 12 May 1984, pp 1470–1472.

4. Tudor Hart, J. The inverse care law. The Lancet, 27 February 1971.

5. Bryant, J. Health and the developing world. Cornell University Press, 1969 and Cornell Paperbacks, 1972.

6. Black, Sir Douglas. An anthology of false antitheses. Rock Carling Fellowship 1984. London, Nuffield Provincial Hospitals Trust, 1984.

INTRODUCTION

Nan Carle

In 1988, an international seminar sponsored by the King's Fund with support from the Kellogg Foundation, brought together top managers from six countries to explore 'Managing for Health Result'. This was not intended to be an easy process, with neat divisions according to political and financial background. And, in the event, whether participants represented health services operating in a free market or in a regulated one of state provision, the debate about defining health result and managing towards it was complex and often confusing. There was heated discussion about whether participants were '*doing the right thing*' or just '*doing things right*'. Was it possible to do both? To consider health result 'independently' of the economics of health care provision is clearly both naive and unrealistic. Yet to attend only to objectives defined by economic values can threaten the quality of care and the health status of individuals, groups of people and even whole communities.

In one way, seminar participants found it simple to define health result: it depended on the perspective of the person speaking. So definitions were many and varied, and with that amount of variety the simplicity changed to complexity. Nowhere was this diversity more pronounced than in the debate about professional management and clinical management. Dieter Kuntz refers in his paper to a telephone survey in which hospital administrators said that doctors were either tinkerers, who wanted to play with the most expensive new gadgetry, or independent thinkers who unrealistically denied that in hospitals they were part of an organisation. Doctors, for their part, said that administrators were reluctant to ask for medical advice on cutting costs, staff or the allocation of resources, while encroaching on issues that should be dealt with by medical staff.

The seminar's arguments about the rights and wrongs of whole systems or of individual perspectives seemed at times sanctimonious and denied the complexities that are easier to unravel from a distance. For example, one of the fundamental tenets of health care, the traditions of the Hippocratic oath, were being severely threatened. Robert Maxwell refers to these dilemmas in his preface; so does Cyril Chantler in his case study of doctors in management at Guy's Hospital in London. Doctors and others who meet patients and clients face to face find it very difficult to consider themselves part of a bigger organisation where priorities must be set for finite resources. Some individuals will receive less than practitioners know it is possible to offer. On the other hand, if whole organisations go back to individuals and do not get beyond to the patterns and trends present in populations, then the individual still loses out in being a part of high quality health care. How these decisions get made and by whom is the root of much of the current tension. My experience is that keeping this tension alive is one of the most important management tasks in times of great uncertainty and change. If either side were to be dampened, or ignored, then we could find ourselves unthinkingly going down very damaging paths in the provision of health care.

Another of the complexities is that there are few if any certainties about what constitutes health. Writing about this in a way that makes sense also raises a whole set of issues. Fortunately, Robert Maxwell's preface addresses clearly the relative and subjective nature of defining health result. Different people are needed at different levels in the system to make reliable judgments about what constitutes quality.

Maxwell handles these uncertainties by offering us a coherent framework for considering health result and ways to manage it. The framework includes six dimensions of health care quality and four

Figure 2.1

MANAGEMENT BUILDING BLOCKS

DIMENSIONS OF HEALTH CARE QUALITY		Assessment of health needs	Formulation of objectives and priorities for intervention	Development and operation of programmes	Assessment of impact
	Access				
	Relevance to needs				
	Effectiveness				
	Equity				
	Social acceptability				
	Efficiency and economy				

20

building blocks for management. I have put them together in the matrix shown in Figure 2.1.

This matrix makes two assumptions. The first is that quality and health result are synonymous. I am assuming that there would be little disagreement that the result for which we should be striving is high quality services for patients and clients who require health care. Robert Maxwell's six dimensions of quality have been well used by managers in Britain to make sense of the complex issues in deciding quality and measuring it. My second assumption is that the four building blocks are basic to good management: assessing the needs of the consumers, setting objectives and priorities for intervention, developing operational programmes and assessing the impact of the work! These seem to me to be unarguable cornerstones of good management practice.

In the following collection of papers, I have used the matrix to plot how each service described managed the turbulence of its organisational context in its search for health result. Each of the ten case studies was written by either a senior medical practitioner or a top manager involved in the delivery of health care. They clearly illustrate the trials and tribulations they faced as they tried to manoeuvre through a specific set of problems. The case studies are separated into sections which relate to the quality dimension that is their main focus. The sections are: ensuring relevance to need; considering efficiency and economy; and seeking equity and social acceptability.

Before each of the papers I have offered a connecting summary and posed a question for the reader to consider while reading the case study. I have used the chart (Figure 2.1) as a reference point for how I judged each of the case studies.

The reflections on what worked and what still posed difficulties are widely relevant to anyone working in health care who is trying to manage under severe financial constraints or considerable organisational change. The writers hope that sharing their experience will help others learn about managing for health result. It is a subject, after all, that affects us all.

ENSURING RELEVANCE TO NEEDS

Occupational health in Petro-Canada Incorporated
Connecting summary

	Assessment of health needs	Formulation of objectives and priorities for intervention	Development and operation of programmes	Assessment of impact
Access				
Relevance to needs				
Effectiveness				
Equity				
Social acceptability				
Efficiency and economy				

One of the more heated debates during the seminar was whether managers were involved in 'doing the right thing' or 'doing things right'. At no time was the group more polarised than during Dr Waddell's presentation of his case study. There was a good deal of discussion about whether occupational health was really about health and health care. The concept of health as 'the optimum fit between the worker and the work place so that work goes on meeting the business objectives of the company' was an uncomfortable one for many of the managers present. Yet I have plotted the case study on the matrix to fill all the building blocks under the quality dimension of relevance to needs. Because of the financial crises within Petro-Canada Incorporated, the practitioner-managers in its occupational health section had to demonstrate the relevance of their work to the need of its employees and also to ensure benefit to the company. The occupational health section had no given right to exist; it faced a real possibility of going out of business. So there were very sharp questions: did the service add real value, or was it 'make up' health care? What would be the real health for individuals if it did go out of business?

Petro-Canada's health care managers developed a strategy which turned occupational health from a 'nice to have' extra into a specific service of added value. They changed the relationship between the company's top managers and their own department and were able to demonstrate the impact of their work and gain credibility.

There are inherent conflicts of interest between serving company needs and the health needs of employees. But is that really very much different from managing for health result within the context of competing priorities among medical consultants in the public sector? What does the reader think?

OCCUPATIONAL HEALTH IN PETRO-CANADA INCORPORATED

Cameron Waddell

This case study deals as much or more with philosophical issues of management as with issues that can be described in largely quantifiable terms. It is the story of how a group of health professionals in a corporate setting managed through a very difficult business reorientation and reorganisation in a major Canadian oil and gas company. It might be more properly called 'a study in survival'.

Petro-Canada Incorporated is one of the largest fully integrated oil and gas companies in Canada and the only one which is wholly Canadian-owned. In 1987, with assets of over $8bn and revenue of over $5bn, it ranked eleventh in the *Financial Post* 500 survey of companies in Canada.

All this appears fairly remarkable, in that the company was only created as a crown corporation by act of parliament in 1975, with a board of directors consisting of senior public servants, people from private sector business and two senior executives of Petro-Canada. The company has built up its broad asset base by acquisition and integration. The government's original intent was to secure Canada's long-term energy requirements through exploitation of frontier resources and investment in non-conventional recovery technologies. In 1984, the emphasis shifted dramatically: the government of that day released the company to behave as a private sector competitor in all aspects of the oil and gas business, to enhance its financial performance and to improve profitability.

In October 1985, Petro-Canada acquired the downstream assets of Gulf Canada, which established it as the second company in the oil and gas sector. Almost immediately, but unrelatedly, unconstrained production of crude oil by OPEC members in the face of generally decreased demand led to a steady fall in oil prices; it was no longer feasible to continue Canadian exploration and production at the then current rate. The only avenue open to the company was to cut expenses.

The Gulf acquisition had brought in some 4,000 employees and much duplication of function. In a very uncomfortable process called 'downsizing', which affected both operations and people, the number of employees fell from 10,193 to 7,204 in a year – a drop of 29 per cent.

Background to change: occupational health

Occupational health involves an ill-defined mixture of clinical medicine, public health practice, counselling psychology, social policy development and implementation, employee relations and occupational hygiene, with results geared towards both employee and business. In Canada, occupational health services are not in competition with the publicly-funded medicare system; they are not there to duplicate services readily available from walk-in clinics, private practitioners, hospitals and other institutions. With the exception of emergency services, primary health care is not a mandate. Companies are third party payers in most health activities. Senior management remains unimpressed with health care costs generally, because of public funding. What does come under its scrutiny is the occupational health budget. Occupational health services in Canada must prove themselves largely in non-clinical areas.

The role of management in occupational health in the private business sector is to ensure the optimum fit between the worker and the workplace so that business objectives continue to be met, to the mutual benefit of employee and employer. The occupational health manager must keep an ethical focus on both these partners. While pursuing health results for employees, either through direct clinical assessment or health policy formulation, the manager must continually demonstrate that his activity contributes to the company's business objectives.

The potential for conflict – and disaster – is obvious. The challenge lies in building a congruence of perspectives between employee and employer so that both productivity and employee relations are enhanced. This demands not just technical expertise, but continuing integration of health issues into the corporation's business plan. Ultimately, this will result in a permanent 'invitation to the strategic party'. The starting point is, as Patrick Pinto suggests, adherence to the Noah principle: predicting rain doesn't help – building arks does.

As Petro-Canada grew, so did the occupational health group. There was little by way of a plan until 1984, when the disjointed service was brought together under a new Corporate medical director. He fired the two full-time physicians and set up a fully-centralised department; all medical resources in the company reported to Calgary. In August 1985, the Corporate Safety Group was amalgamated with Corporate Health to form Corporate Health and Safety. The safety group had a purely central advisory function. This organisation (see

27

Figure 3.1) continued through the acquisition of Gulf and was being rationalised when 'downsizing' was imposed.

At the end of March 1986, the medical director announced that he was leaving the company. Health and Safety was amalgamated with Corporate Security, with a director of health, safety and security. The new department's budget of $8.3m was arbitrarily cut by 40 per cent to $5.0m and the staff complement was to be cut by the same percentage (from 94.5 people to 57) by the end of the year. Decisions were quickly made and, in May 1986, the new department was in place with budgets redrawn and the planned reduction of personnel (see Figure 3.2).

Position analysis

This period was quite traumatic in both a business and a psychological sense. All but essential activity ceased throughout the company; personal fears overshadowed all work and survival became the topic of the day. The occupational health group had to chart a course through the difficulties to emerge with as intact a programme and team as possible. This demanded a rigorous look at the group's record and current constraints. Three issues needed immediate and simultaneous attention:

1. *Credibility*

The former medical director was very ambitious and driving, with a largely administrative background and a heavy leaning towards health promotion. This had been a fair shock to the management, which had been used to very low key medical involvement. Although the medical director gained the support of the executive council, it is unlikely that he won individuals emotionally. 'If you didn't talk about stress we wouldn't have any in this company' was one comment from the executive vice-president. 'I don't like being told I've got no options', said the chief executive officer.

A major thrust of the original programme was to set up a computerised health information system. Over two years, there had been few results and escalating costs. When funds were withdrawn, the project was to have cost $490,000 in capital and another $50,000 in revenue.

With little group support and unclear purpose, the manager for industrial hygiene funded a study of business hazards in the workplace. This cost $50,000, served no purpose and was a summary of information readily available from standard sources.

The medical director recognised the sagging image of the department and contracted a public relations firm to develop a departmental strategy. The outcome was $30,000 spent and a departmental motto – 'commitment in action'.

As these anecdotes show, the department was adept at trying to add bells and whistles, but had not concentrated on building a solid occupational health base. The orientation appeared to be towards process within the department rather than towards outcomes for employees and the business. There was no mechanism for feeding back information to management on the health of the workforce, or to employees on individual health. The concern was to meet legislated requirements only.

2. *Integration with corporate security*

This was very difficult. The departure of the medical director offered the vice-president for human resources the opportunity to reduce his direct reports. The new director of health safety and security is a former police officer, oriented towards information-seeking and control. He set up the new organisation with little input from below. His scanty knowledge of occupational health required long sessions of explanation and, at times, justification. He once summed up his attitude towards professionals with 'I'm not impressed with professional credentials'. There was trouble at the manager level and great difficulty trying to integrate the support staff who still felt loyal to their former working relationships. The one area of agreement was the confidentiality of medical information. This was non-negotiable to both the health group and the new director. Health information remained secure.

3. *Morale*

It should be evident that the whole situation was demoralising. The group lost 40 per cent of its budget and 40 per cent of its people. The medical director who led the group left to pursue personal ambition. The group was forced into marriage with a strange bedfellow. There was little professional satisfaction. Clearly occupational health had little status.

But as in most crises, there was opportunity. The approach had to extend beyond the more or less traditional roles of administration into business strategy. The shifting corporate environment offered many advantages. The challenge was to become very selective in resource expenditure so that a high quality contribution would eventually speak for itself. The starting point was accepting the reality and gaining a solid understanding of the business of Petro-Canada.

Figure 3.1   Pre-reorganisation

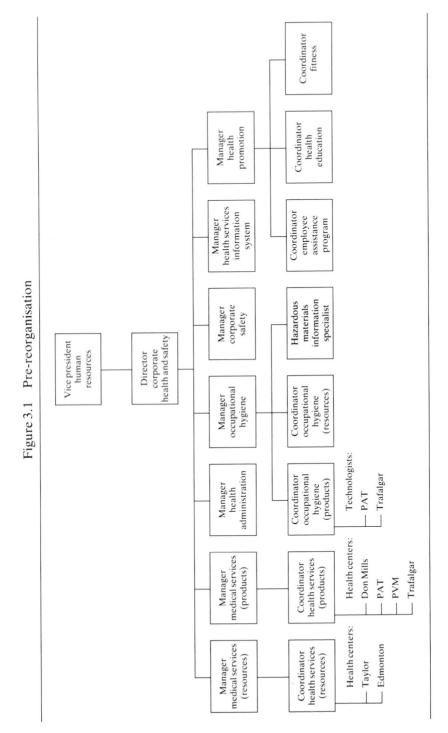

Figure 3.2   Post-reorganisation

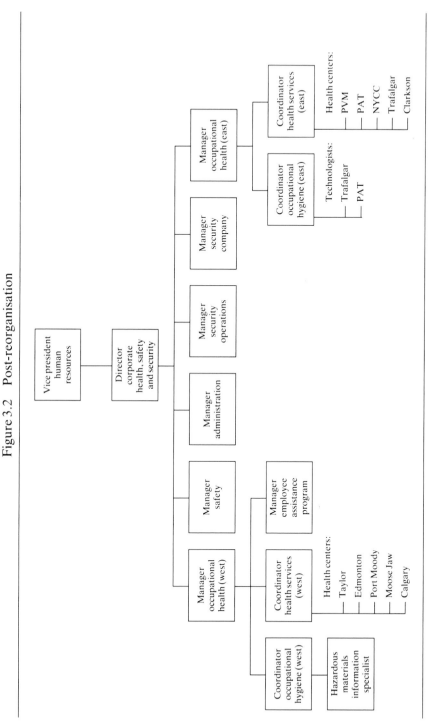

Developing the strategic approach

Dedicated teamwork became the norm, perhaps because there was no alternative; there was too much work to do. Duplication and re-inventing wheels gave place to partnership, division of work, respect and open invitations to problem-solving. Capitalising on individual strengths led to rotating leadership and then naturally to brainstorming towards solutions.

Back to basics became the thrust of activity. 'Nice to have' services, such as voluntary medical examinations, were dropped in favour of a risk-based approach to health monitoring. It was simply too expensive and grossly irrational to examine everyone, every year, for everything. Regulatory requirements were the starting point, with a comprehensive programme development in each area. Worksites were assessed for risks or hazards beyond statutory requirements and codes of practice were developed. The expectations identified to service providers were for high quality services in field locations, with minimal disruption of operations. Results, not activities were identified as achievements and communication of results to stakeholders was considered essential.

'Value-added' became a criterion for determining commitment to a particular project. Occupational health is a cost to the organisation and whatever is done must in some way contribute to reducing or offsetting that cost. The benefit of the employee assistance programme, for instance, was well realised during 'downsizing', as it helped redundant employees with individual counselling and offered group stress management sessions.

Building on success is a time-honoured approach. Petro-Canada has had a modest international component, with a correspondingly modest contribution from occupational health. The five-step programme to support the Corporation's international travellers became the model for a human resource support programme to the whole international operation when that expanded.

Bias towards the future is essential to credibility. Senior management does not like surprises, mostly because they tend to be negative. A constant watch must be kept on impending legislation, social policy issues and scientific advances. It became obvious, for instance, that the federal government was getting serious about chemical hazards in the workplace and that a workplace hazardous materials information system would be required by law. Work was started so that the company was in compliance on the implementation date. This proactive stance not only led to the health result of protecting our workers, but maintained the company's competitiveness by ensuring that its chemical product could continue to be marketed.

Targets of opportunity were constantly sought, beyond the establishment of a basic foundation of occupational health programmes. The smoke-free workplace issue was identified early on as an opportunity to establish a win/win outcome for both management and employees. The social climate in Canada was clearly anti-smoking and the only hurdle was to have senior management approval. After seven months, Petro-Canada workplaces across the country were smoke-free.

Structure versus politics

The place of power and politics in this Corporation cannot be over-emphasised. When the business of the organisation is not health and when the health group becomes submerged organisationally, political strategy becomes a weapon of survival.

In the restructuring and reorientation of the occupational health group, there develops a sensitivity to the politics of the organisation. It is relatively easy to design programmes from a position of technical expertise, using scientific and statutory building blocks. But if this were all that is required, the former occupational health group should have been feeling successful.

That group was well-organised in a technical management sense. What was missing was personal contact with both the field and senior executives – contact that would allow ventilation of biases and alignment of goals. Organisations are made up of people, and to win people there must be trust. Impersonal policies and medical expertise may be acknowledged, but tend to be ignored in practice unless an imminent threat is perceived. The previous thrust of occupational health, which relied almost exclusively on position power, was replaced with an emphasis on personal power.

Developing the programmed approach

There did not appear to be a workable standard model to apply to our circumstances. What evolved was based on the management strategy and style identified above. Realising who we serve and how we serve them generated a simple quality assurance model. Figure 3.3 is the model applied to the hearing conservation programme (Western Canada), indicating its initial status. With a view of occupational health programming that encompasses structure, process and outcome, it pointed up the failure and allowed concentration on outcomes. Health professionals tend to be very good at setting structures, gearing up processes and generating outputs. But outputs are not outcomes. Our outcomes focus on our clients and how we serve them, which is information delivery. The power of information is immense and, when passed on in comprehensible terms, leads to empowered clients (employees and management) as partners.

In the business environment, the alternative to action was stagnation. The usual approach of developing policy and having it ratified by senior management was abandoned. Under a common law approach, detailed occupational health codes of practice were developed, based on the quality assurance model. Our premise was that we would be judged by what we did rather than by what we said we did. It became essential to stop speaking in 'medicine' and to start conversing in 'business'. With individual employees, the traditional professional-patient covenant prevailed, but we set a new tack to empower managers to effect health result.

Managing for health result

In 1987, employees at a natural gas production plant in Alberta were monitored according to the hearing evaluation code of practice and it was discovered that four per cent had an early warning shift in hearing threshold. In 1988, 30 per cent of employees at the plant had such a shift, which is double the set limit of 10 per cent.

The site manager was made aware of this result, as a partner, and no further involvement of occupational health was required. Health result had equal priority in his overall operation and he took ownership of the problem. Several engineering modifications had taken place at the plant without requisite safeguards for hearing protection. These were corrected and the hazard level reduced.

The southern production district of Alberta comprises a large geographic area with several natural gas production plants; 26 employees drove company vehicles between sites as a major part of their job, with the window rolled down in the very hot summer months. A survey showed dangerous levels of noise exposure while driving with open windows. A complementary look at the drivers' hearing showed that ten of them had definite hearing loss and three borderline loss, with a greater loss in the left ear than the right in 11 out of 13. This was enough for a local management initiative, even though it was certainly not a rigorous causal study. The outcome was a business decision to purchase only air-conditioned vehicles. The desired health outcome was met, but with additional positive client outcomes in quality of working life.

34

Figure 3.3   Hearing conservation – Western Canada

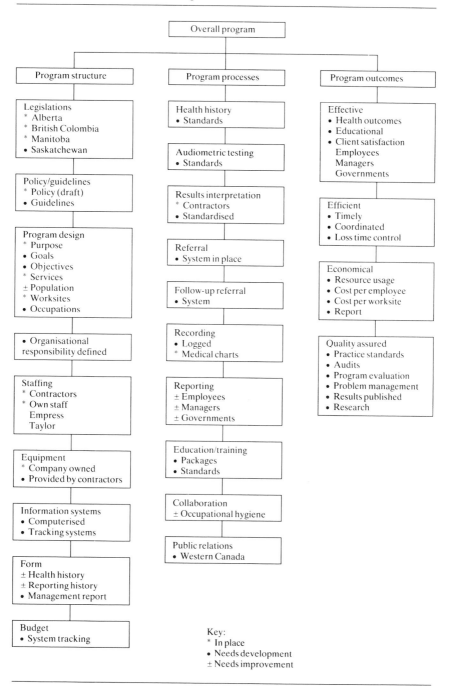

Overall program

Program structure

Legislations
* Alberta
* British Colombia
* Manitoba
• Saskatchewan

Policy/guidelines
* Policy (draft)
• Guidelines

Program design
* Purpose
• Goals
• Objectives
* Services
± Population
* Worksites
• Occupations

• Organisational
responsibility defined

Staffing
* Contractors
* Own staff
  Empress
  Taylor

Equipment
* Company owned
• Provided by contractors

Information systems
• Computerised
• Tracking systems

Form
± Health history
± Reporting history
• Management report

Budget
• System tracking

Program processes

Health history
• Standards

Audiometric testing
• Standards

Results interpretation
* Contractors
• Standardised

Referral
• System in place

Follow-up referral
• System

Recording
• Logged
* Medical charts

Reporting
± Employees
± Managers
± Governments

Education/training
• Packages
• Standards

Collaboration
± Occupational hygiene

Public relations
• Western Canada

Program outcomes

Effective
• Health outcomes
• Educational
• Client satisfaction
  Employees
  Managers
  Governments

Efficient
• Timely
• Coordinated
• Loss time control

Economical
• Resource usage
• Cost per employee
• Cost per worksite
• Report

Quality assured
• Practice standards
• Audits
• Program evaluation
• Problem management
• Results published
• Research

Key:
* In place
• Needs development
± Needs improvement

Interim conclusion

Managing for health result in the defined population of Petro-Canada through a severe business downturn was a daily challenge which has not yet abated. The key to our survival has been not the technical content of our work but the nature of our interaction with our clients. It is management style which has made the difference: the sense of an intradepartmental team, client-focused partnership and empowerment of both through problem-sharing. The group has developed confidence in this approach and extended programmes beyond strictly statutory requirements. Building arks seems to have drawn people's attention. But we wait patiently for the permanent 'invitation to the strategic party'.

Health for all in Bloomsbury
Connecting summary

	Assessment of health needs	Formulation of objectives and priorities for intervention	Development and operation of programmes	Assessment of impact
Access				
Relevance to needs	▒	▒	▒	▒
Effectiveness				
Equity				
Social acceptability				
Efficiency and economy				

I chose to plot the main focus of Alasdair Liddell's case study, like Cameron Waddell's, as ensuring relevance to needs. As in Waddell's case history, this focus seemed to be a matter of survival. There are, however, some major differences. In theory at least, district health authorities in England do not go out of business. People have a guaranteed right to health care. Health is seen as a right, not a privilege. Nevertheless, the dire financial constraints of Bloomsbury Health Authority meant that real questions were being asked about how far resources could be redistributed and how the authority could continue to provide even the existing health services.

Another major difference between the two situations was in the approaches to solving the problems. Bloomsbury Health Authority chose to use the principles embodied in the World Health Organization's 'health for all' – a set of targets for the year 2000 which, if met, would enable the world's entire population to be healthy enough to lead a socially and economically productive life. Bloomsbury used these targets to help it focus on outcomes rather than just on management input and process.

Some of the American seminar participants called this 'fatuous'. 'Like weather for all' was one comment. Once more, there was debate about 'doing the right thing' and 'doing things right' and the advantages and disadvantages of both courses. Important questions were asked: how could managers demonstrate that their actions made a real difference to the lives of people they served; could managers deliver 'health for all' when very basic needs – for example, decent housing – were not being met? Like the previous case study, this one focused not only on the quality dimension of 'relevance to need' but on all four management building blocks. Bloomsbury Health Authority had undertaken an assessment of local needs and organisational responsibility.

The authority had to make a cut of £6m and authority members were not at all eager to do this. One of the features of the management process was to set about developing a new culture so that judgments about future allocation could be better informed. What does the reader think of this: does it show courage or folly?

HEALTH FOR ALL IN BLOOMSBURY

Alasdair Liddell

This case study explores some of the practical difficulties of managing for health result in an inner city authority operating under severe resource constraint. It examines two related issues: the application of 'health for all' principles to the planning and management of health services, and the development of a culture of evaluation through the appointment of a director of evaluation. It also raises some key questions which reflect the tensions that arise from an attempt to shift from traditional values to those underpinning 'health for all'. These include the tension between health needs and financial constraint and the tension between a local service to a defined community and a specialist service to a mostly scattered population; the challenge of achieving genuine management commitment to health result; and the difficulty of measuring progress.

Bloomsbury Health Authority is one of a dozen district health authorities (DHAs) in central London. Its role is to provide comprehensive services to a local population; a range of specialist services to a wider population; facilities for teaching doctors, nurses and other health professionals, and for research. The Authority has an annual revenue budget of £135m and employs some 8,500 staff. In terms of resources, it is one of the largest district health authorities in England, but its resident population (135,000) and its geographical size (16 sq km) are relatively small.

The Authority manages 15 hospitals (with between 32 and 650 beds), three health centres and a number of community-based health clinics. Much of this accommodation is very old, in poor repair and unsuitable for its present purpose. The Authority has recently authorised a major feasibility study on replacing its scattered acute hospital services with a completely new 900-bed teaching hospital on a single site.

Background to change

Organisational geography

Bloomsbury Health Authority was formed in 1982 from five organisations: two teaching districts (adjacent but in separate health regions and supporting two undergraduate medical schools) and three single-specialty postgraduate groups of hospitals, together with their associated academic institutes. Each of these organisations had different systems, procedures and cultures.

In 1988, the undergraduate medical schools and the postgraduate institutes were brought together into a single school of medicine, organised into two faculties (medical sciences and clinical sciences) of University College, one of the most powerful multi-faculty colleges of London University.

The district covers part of two local authorities, which have markedly different politics and priorities, and each of which, in turn, relates to at least one other health authority.

Local needs

The local resident population has special needs which reflect inner city living conditions. There are large numbers of elderly people living alone, unskilled workers, single parent families and unemployed people from outside the UK. There are high rates of drug and alcohol abuse and of psychiatric morbidity, and large numbers of homeless and rootless people in bed and breakfast accommodation, in hostels, or on the streets. (See Appendix 1 for further information.)

Existing services and support mechanisms are inadequate to meet these needs. Primary care services are uneven in quality, with more than a third of general practitioners working single-handed and more than a fifth aged over 60. Family and social support is undermined by very high population mobility and migration of family carers out of inner London. There are problems of access to services for the ethnic minority communities – particularly Bengalis, Afro-Caribbeans, Greek Cypriots and Chinese.

Specialist services and educational responsibilities

The school of medicine has an annual intake of 200 undergraduates and there are extensive postgraduate programmes particularly, but not exclusively, in the three postgraduate specialties (orthopaedics, urology/nephrology and ENT). The school of nursing has 680 places for basic training and also provides post-basic courses for an average of 360 students a year. There are schools of radiography, physiotherapy and the only NHS school of chiropody.

The regional and postgraduate specialties account for some 40 per cent of admissions to the district's hospitals. But even in the local acute specialties – which are ostensibly provided in every district hospital – there are many 'unrecognised' specialisms which attract pa-

Table 4.1   Local acute specialties: admissions to Bloomsbury 1986

	Immediate		Planned		Total	
Bloomsbury residents	4,105	15%	2,661	10%	6,766	25%
Neighbouring districts	1,835	7%	1,833	7%	3,668	13%
Others	5,499	20%	11,374	42%	16,873	62%
Total	11,439	42%	15,868	58%	27,307	100%

tients from far afield (see Table 4.1).

Partly because of its location, but also because of its special expertise, the authority is responsible for services to 15 per cent of the country's AIDS patients (December 1987). Examples of specialist services include the Elizabeth Garrett Anderson Hospital (where women can be treated exclusively by women staff), the Royal London Homeopathic Hospital and the Margaret Pyke Centre, the country's largest training and research centre for family planning.

Pressures for change

The creation of Bloomsbury provided the opportunity and need for change, irrespective of any pressure from resource constraint. There has been significant progress in rationalising and unifying services and support functions. There is now one obstetric service, for example, and one accident and emergency department; a programme to unify and rehouse the pathology service is well under way.

Change is also needed to achieve service improvements. There have been national initiatives to shorten waiting lists and to provide screening for breast and cervical cancer; regional initiatives to replace major mental illness and mental handicap hospitals with locally-based community services; and, above all, the local requirement to meet identified needs and to plug gaps in service.

During the three years to March 1988, Bloomsbury achieved savings of some £13m (about 10 per cent of its annual allocation) and a further £4.2m savings were programmed for 1988/89. But the authority still faced a budget deficit of some £5.5m which could only be resolved by major reductions in service. So, over recent years, it is resource constraints which have been the major pressure for change and the major management preoccupation.

This pressure has come from three main sources:

explicit national and regional policy to shift resources to provide equity of access both geographically and between care groups;

41

reductions in spending power, arising from persistent underfunding of inflation (1.25 per cent in 1987/8, 4 per cent over the previous five years) and rising standards set by legislation or the training authorities;

the need for internal investment to fund development of priority care services and to develop organisational capacity – by investing in information systems, for example.

Managing for health result

Heath for all in Bloomsbury

In February 1986, the Bloomsbury Health Authority endorsed the World Health Organization's 'health for all' (HFA) strategy, and asked for annual reports on the health status of Bloomsbury residents and on progress towards the HFA targets. HFA has become an integral part of the planning and management process in the district. The emphasis on health status is important, because it focuses on outcome rather than, as more traditionally, on input and process, and because it provides a basis for measuring performance. (Appendix 2 gives further information about 'health for all'.)

Each year, district health authorities prepare an operational plan (short-term programme), broadly according to the following cycle:

May: issue planning guidelines
June–August: prepare draft plan
September–November: public consultation
December: plan finalised
February–March: budgets prepared
1 April: plan and budgets implemented

If all goes well, each stage reflects the previous one.

In February 1987, the first Bloomsbury 'health for all' annual report reviewed the health status of the local population and drew out the various health promotion initiatives which were planned or in progress in the district. This provided an overall context for the preparation of the 1988 operational plan and an important source for specific guidelines. The second annual report, in February 1988, reviewed progress and provided a forward context for the 1989 plan.

Equity in health

The authority has expressed its commitment to equity by planning to meet the special needs of vulnerable groups, the disadvantaged and the underserved. A key mechanism for this has been the establishment of a 'development fund' to enable the transfer of a progressive 0.5 per cent (£0.65m) annually from acute to priority services. This shift has meant reductions in the acute hospital sector.

Initiatives include:

development of an information package on 'caring in a multi-racial society' as a basis of staff training programme;

development of interpreting, and introduction of advocacy services;

improvements in services for homeless people and hostel-dwellers;

transfer of mental health facilities from remote institutions to locally-oriented, community-based facilities;

appointment of an equal opportunities adviser and initiatives to improve equal opportunities in employment.

Health promotion

Initiatives include:

development of screening for breast and cervical cancer;

implementation of food and health policy within health service premises and extension to other workplaces;

establishment of staff counselling service.

Consumer participation

Initiatives include:

CASPE 'information from patients' project;

development of local planning;

review of patient information booklets.

Multi-sectoral collaboration

Initiatives include:

publication of 'GP directory' and regular GP newsletter;

work with adjacent health authorities on common health problems (especially services for people with learning difficulties);

work with family practitioner committees on primary care and community services.

Primary care

Initiatives include:

extension of community midwifery service to Bengali community;

funding two new health centre projects.

Evaluation in Bloomsbury

The health sector's traditional weakness is its inability to fund any real measure of how well it is doing. If management is the manipulation of resources to produce benefits, and if benefits in the health context are improvements to the quality of life, how do we measure that?

In Bloomsbury, the top management post of director of evaluation was created with a brief to:

promote a culture of evaluation within the district;

develop measures of effectiveness;

evaluate changes in patterns of care and service provision;

assess consumers' views of health services;

provide, eventually, an evaluative basis for choice and decisions on resource allocation.

The objective was to develop an approach which would allow general managers to respond to two questions: how effective are we in improving the quality of our patients' lives, and what can we learn from their experience of receiving health care in Bloomsbury? The objective has been pursued in a number of ways, including the 'health for all' initiative, the development of locality planning and the CASPE information from patients project.

CASPE information from patients

This project – one of six funded by the NHS Management Board – seeks to assess consumer satisfaction in a way which is continuous, comprehensive (covering treatment and care as well as environment and support services), and allows management to focus on detailed changes in quality and on specific aspects of the service. Simple questionnaires allow the calculation of a 'satisfaction index' on about 15 aspects of the service, in a way which can be analysed by computer. Every patient gets a form before discharge.

The satisfaction index can be compared in time and between wards (or even consultants). Supplementary questions can examine problem areas, expose the impact of specific changes or serve clinical research purposes. This gives management a powerful tool for assessing the quality of service. But it also puts management on the spot, since success or failure in improving quality can be quantified with uncomfortable clarity!

Questions arising

Can health services managers or professionals have any real impact on the health status of the community, given that factors which influence it – like housing, employment, nutrition, tobacco, alcohol and accidents – are largely outside their control?

Can a 'health for all' approach be more than peripheral in a district whose local community accounts for only 25 per cent of its hospital activity?

How can policies for promoting health, which depend on reorienting the approach of strongly traditional institutions, be effectively pursued under severe resource constraint?

How can clinicians be influenced to take more account of health?

How can managers make 'health for all' a genuine management commitment?

How can managers be held accountable for pursuing 'health for all'?

Appendix 1   Bloomsbury Health Authority – additional profile information

Table 4.2   Resident population environment: population projections for Bloomsbury HA

Age	1986	2001	
0-14	13,300	18,540	+ 39%
15-64	92,080	89,390	− 3%
65-84	19,620	14,570	− 26%
85+	2,290	2,850	+ 24%
Total	127,290	125,350	− 1.5%

Source: OPCS

Table 4.3   Demographic characteristics in Bloomsbury compared with England and Wales

Demographic variable	Bloomsbury %	England and Wales
% Children 0-14	10.5	20.3
% Elderly 65+	18.9	15.3
% Pensioners alone	10.2	5.3
% Unskilled workers	6.1	4.5
% Single parent families	2.8	2.2
% Poor housing	7.1	3.3
% Overcrowding	11.9	7.3
% Mobility	17.2	9.7
% Born outside UK	31.1	10.0 (in Greater London)
% Unemployed	17.0 - 19.9	13.0 - 14.0
% Homeless	>2.5	>1.0 (in Greater London)

Source: 1981 Census

Table 4.4   Housing in Camden

	LA owned	Housing association	Private landlord	Owner occupied	Total
Unfit for habitation	1,550	1,200	5,800	2,450	11,000
Lacking basic amenities	600	100	1,050	350	2,100
In need of renovation	8,300	300	4,050	2,950	15,600

Total domestic dwellings approximately   8,500

Note: Figures are rounded
Source: Report to Camden Council Housing Department, November 1987

Table 4.5   Health status statistics, 1985 and 1986

	Bloomsbury		NE Thames Region		England and Wales	
	1985	1986	1985	1986	1985	1986
Crude death rate (deaths/1000 pop)	12.1	11.8	11.3	10.9	11.8	11.6
Standardised mortality ratio	90	92	96	95	100	100
Deaths from:						
Coronary heart disease	344	350				
Lung cancer	121	108				
Strokes	153	134				
Accidents	76	88				
Cervical cancer	8	3				
Birth rate (births/100 pop)	11.5	12.8	13.9	14.1	13.1	13.2
Perinatal deaths	15	20				
Perinatal mortality rate	10.0	11.8	9.3	9.6	9.8	9.6

Table 4.6   Perinatal mortality, 1981-1986

	1981	1982	1983	1984	1985	1986
Bloomsbury:						
Stillbirths	7	8	8	13	13	12
Deaths in 1st week	5	8	7	5	2	8
Perinatal mortality rate	9.7	11.4	10.3	11.3	9.3	11.8
NE Thames Region	11.0	11.6	9.9	9.7	10.0	9.6
England and Wales	11.8	11.3	10.4	10.1	9.8	9.6

Source: SD52

Table 4.7   Deaths in Bloomsbury under the age of 65, 1981-1985

Cause of death	Deaths	Years of* life lost	Average years lost
Coronary heart disease	352	6,600	21
Asthma, bronchitis and emphysema	55	1,015	18
Stroke	106	2,100	20
Cancer of the cervix	18	460	26
Cancer of the bronchus and lung	176	2,970	17
Accidents and external injuries	293	10,395	35
Total	1,000	23,540	

*Assuming a life expectancy of 75

Figure 4.1   Deprivation in Bloomsbury by electoral ward using the Jarman combined index of eight variables based on the 1981 census

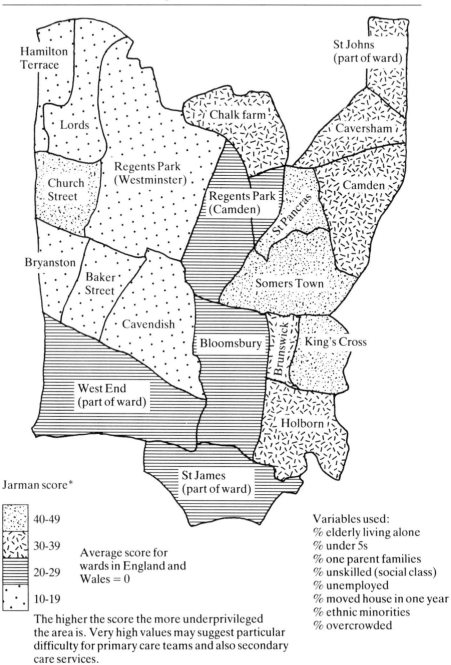

Hamilton Terrace

St Johns (part of ward)

Lords

Chalk farm

Caversham

Regents Park (Westminster)

Church Street

Regents Park (Camden)

Camden

St Pancras

Bryanston

Baker Street

Somers Town

Cavendish

Bloomsbury

Brunswick

King's Cross

West End (part of ward)

Holborn

St James (part of ward)

Jarman score*

40-49

30-39   Average score for wards in England and
20-29   Wales = 0

10-19

The higher the score the more underprivileged the area is. Very high values may suggest particular difficulty for primary care teams and also secondary care services.

Variables used:
% elderly living alone
% under 5s
% one parent families
% unskilled (social class)
% unemployed
% moved house in one year
% ethnic minorities
% overcrowded

48

Appendix 2   Health for all

In May 1977, the 30th World Health Assembly resolved that:

'the main social target of Governments and WHO in the coming decades should be the attainment by all citizens of the world by the year 2000 of a level of health that will permit them to lead a socially and economically productive life'.

This approach was prompted by a recognition of the two basic facts that:

despite increases in resources spent on health, and significant medical and technological developments, people's level of health is far lower than it could be;

there remain significant inequalities in health in terms of geography, care group and social class.

In 1980, the WHO European Region adopted a strategy for attaining 'health for all' within the region. This outlined four main areas of concern:

lifestyles and health;

risk factors affecting health and the environment;

reorientation of the health care system itself;

the political, management, technological, manpower and research support necessary to achieve changes in these areas.

The Regional strategy called for:

higher priority to be given to health promotion and disease prevention;

all sectors (not only health services) with an impact on health to take positive steps to maintain and improve it;

more stress to be placed on the role of individuals, families and communities in health development;

primary health care to be adopted as the major approach to achieving these changes.

Health is defined as a positive condition, involving the whole person in his or her context. The WHO concept of health requires a state of physical, mental, emotional and social well-being, not just an absence of disease or disability. 'Health for all' requires mechanisms which shift the focus from disease as a biological deviation from the norm to health as a positive value.

The strategy incorporates four objectives:

to ensure equity in health by reducing the gap in health status within and between communities;

to add life to years by the full development of personal, physical, mental and emotional capacity;

to add health to life by reducing disease and disability;

to add years to life by reducing premature deaths and increasing life expectancy.

A number of important themes underpin the 'health for all' approach:

Equity – to reduce the inequalities between and within communities.

Health promotion – to generate a positive sense of health.

Consumer participation – that is, a well informed, well motivated and actively participating community.

Multi-sectoral collaboration – to ensure the prerequisites for health (food, education, water and sanitation, housing and employment), promote healthy policies and reduce risks in the physical, economic and social environment.

Primary care focus – to meet basic health needs close to where people live and work, in a way which is accessible and acceptable to all.

Planning cancer services in South Australia
Connecting Summary

	Assessment of health needs	Formulation of objectives and priorities for intervention	Development and operation of programmes	Assessment of impact
Access				
Relevance to needs				
Effectiveness				
Equity				
Social acceptability				
Efficiency and economy				

Brendon Kearney's case study on planning cancer services offers a concrete example of combining medicine and management. As such, it falls squarely into the quality dimension of relevance to needs. The paper follows a logical path through each of the building blocks of assessment, setting objectives and priorities, developing operational programmes and assessing their impact. Kearney's presentation of his research highlighted an increase of 23 per cent over seven years in the number of people developing cancer. There were some frightening statistics on the number of people developing cancer through smoking and how long it would take to decrease treatment costs even if everyone stopped smoking now. This engendered a great deal of discussion among seminar participants on whether to give priority to preventive or to palliative forms of treatments.

As a medical manager, Kearney was forced to consider regularly where to invest his time and talent, and so was continually making judgments about the relevance of his work to people's needs and what he considered the most important public health issues. His work contrasts with Liddell's discussion: here the emphasis is on relevance of services to one particular patient group rather than to a total population. And they are each looking at different time scales for visible results. The tension is between doing 'the right thing' for the present or for the future. What are the reader's biases?

5

PLANNING CANCER SERVICES IN SOUTH AUSTRALIA

Brendon Kearney

As the population of South Australia ages, the incidence of new cases of cancer is expected to rise by a quarter within a decade. This paper looks at the role of health service managers in responding to this major challenge, with particular emphasis on the approach of the comprehensive cancer care centre. It also outlines national standards for Australian cancer services.

The Royal Adelaide Hospital/Institute of Medical and Veterinary Science is a 1,000-bed teaching hospital and laboratory complex associated with the University of Adelaide school of medicine. It is the major public institutional provider of health services for South Australia (population 1.4m) including the capital city Adelaide (population 1m). The hospital also serves the Northern Territory, western New South Wales and Victoria. In addition, it is the state's main provider of super-specialty services; these include the state's radiation oncology facilities and the bone marrow transplantation as part of the haematology unit. Medical and surgical oncology services are provided throughout the metropolitan area, but the major services are at the Royal Adelaide Hospital.

The hospital is regarded as an international centre of excellence in the treatment of bone marrow transplantation, following the discovery that circulating blood contains normal stem cells which can be isolated and concentrated and reinfused into the patient. The advent of autologous bone marrow transplantation has led to an increase in the number of patients who can be cured of leukaemia and to the elimination of some nasty side effects of transplantation and the reduction of length of stay and cost of treatment.

Basic research at the Institute of Medical and Veterinary Science has led to the discovery of substances and cell receptors that regulate the growth of cells. A study of the biochemistry of fibrin and migration of cells resulted in the production of a monoclonal antibody which blocks the metastatic process of malignant melanoma cells. Both these discoveries have major diagnostic and therapeutic importance.

Background to change

Over the past 30 years, the age-adjusted death rate for all causes in South Australia has reduced by 25 per cent. The cancer death rate, however, has increased by 35 per cent for males and remained stable for females. The proportion of deaths due to cancer has increased from 17 per cent in 1970 to 25 per cent in 1985.

The incidence of new cases of cancer in South Australia between 1977 and 1984 increased by 23 per cent. When this percentage is standardised for age and sex, it falls to 4.5 per cent. The continued ageing of the population is expected to produce a further increase of 25 per cent in the number of new cases of cancer during the next decade.

The leading causes of cancer deaths in males between 1977 and 1986 were lung (28.4 per cent) colon and rectum (12.5 per cent) and prostate (10.5 per cent). In females, it was breast (19 per cent) colon and rectum (16.3 per cent) and lung (8.5 per cent). But mortality data tend to underestimate grossly the total burden of cancer in the community. While there were 21,674 deaths from cancer between 1977 and 1986, the number of new invasive cancers during that period was almost double that figure (41,757). The main types of cancer in males were lung (18 per cent) prostate (16 per cent) and colon and rectum (14 per cent). In females, they were breast (24.4. per cent) colon and rectum (15.6 per cent) and melanoma (7.6 per cent).

Time trends in cancer incidence between 1977 and 1986 show:

A significant increase among females with no significant change in males.

An increase for males (47 per cent) and females (173 per cent) of cancer of the lip due to sun exposure.

A decrease in stomach cancer in females (31 per cent) with no change in males. This is thought to be due to changes in diet, particularly complex carbohydrates and salted, pickled and smoked foods; the introduction of refrigeration and other non-chemical means of food preservation have played a part.

An increase of cancer of the rectum in males (28 per cent) but no change in females. Colon and rectal cancer are thought to be associated with a high fat, low fibre diet.

A decrease of cancer of the pancreas for both sexes (20 per cent).

A decrease in lung cancer in males (17 per cent) and an increase in females (41 per cent). This reflects the changed pattern of cigarette smoking over the past 30 years.

An increase of melanoma, due to sun exposure and possibly ozone changes, in both sexes (25 per cent).

A decrease in multiple myeloma in males but not in females.

For a fuller picture, see Tables 5.1, 5.2, 5.3 and 5.4.

Table 5.1

	1977	1978	1979	1980	1981	1982	1983	1984
Number of new cases of cancer per annum	3,678	3,782	3,822	4,071	4,109	4,189	4,311	4,518
Standardised by age and sex to 1981 population	3,050	3,070	3,040	3,170	3,110	3,100	3,120	3,190

Stages of cancer treatment

Six stages of cancer treatment can be identified: prevention (primary and secondary); diagnosis and early detection; treatment (curative and palliative); rehabilitation; continuing management; and hospice and palliative care.

For *primary prevention* to be effective, four criteria need to be met:

the risk factors are strongly and causally related to the cancer;

the risk factors are readily identifiable;

the risk factors are readily subject to favourable manipulation;

the cost of identifying and manipulating the risk factors is reasonable.

Lifestyle and behavioural factors could be responsible for up to 60 per cent of cancers. Cigarette smoking, the best-known cause of cancer mortality, is the chief single avoidable cause of death in our society and the most important public health issue of our time. In Australia, sunlight exposure is responsible for a dramatic increase in melanoma and non-melanoma skin cancer. Dietary habits are estimated to account for up to 35 per cent of cancer deaths, but as the above criteria cannot be met, a specific prevention programme (apart from general nutritional advice) cannot be formulated. Occupational exposure to carcinogens represents a small but specific and controllable cause of cancer; regulatory and other approaches to occupational health are essential to eliminate this risk. Finally, sexual behaviour is now thought to be responsible for cervical cancer and AIDS-related cancer deaths.

Table 5.2 Cancer mortality 1986

South Australian Cancer Registry: mortality from cancer, 1986. Number of deaths, the percentage distribution, and the crude mortality rates per 100,000 males and females for some leading sites.*

Males (1986)				Females (1986)			
Site	No	%	Rate	Site	No	%	Rate
Total number	1,330	100.0	193.3	Total number	1,077	100.0	155.0
Lung	366	27.5	53.2	Breast	207	19.2	29.7
Prostate	137	10.3	19.9	Lung	104	9.6	14.9
Colon	108	8.1	15.7	Colon	101	9.3	14.5
Stomach	89	6.6	12.9	Ovary	69	6.4	9.9
Rectum and RS jt				Pancreas	64	5.9	9.2
and anal canal	77	5.7	11.2	Rectum and RS jt			
Pancreas	59	4.4	8.5	and anal canal	59	5.4	8.4
Lymphomas	53	3.9	7.7	Lymphomas	50	4.6	7.2
Bladder	50	3.7	7.2	Stomach	39	3.6	5.6
Leukaemias	42	3.1	6.1	Leukaemias	34	3.1	4.8
Kidney and ureters	41	3.0	5.9	Brain	26	2.4	3.7
Brain	40	3.0	5.8	Cervix	26	2.4	3.7
Melanoma skin	30	2.2	4.3	Corpus uteri	25	2.3	3.6
Oesophagus	23	1.7	3.3	Melanoma skin	21	1.9	3.0
				Bladder	17	1.5	2.4
				Kidney and ureters	17	1.5	2.4
				Oesophagus	14	1.3	2.0

*SA estimated population, ABS 1986

Table 5.3 Cancer incidence 1986

South Australian Cancer Registry: incidence of invasive cancer, 1986. Number of new cases, the percentage distribution and the crude incidence rates per 100,000 males and females for some leading sites.*

Males (1986)				Females (1986)			
Site	No	%	Rate	Site	No	%	Rate
Total number	2,460	100.0	357.6	Total number	2,101	100.0	302.4
Prostate	402	16.3	58.4	Breast	509	24.2	73.2
Lung	397	16.1	57.7	Colon	212	10.0	30.5
Colon	220	8.9	31.9	Melanoma skin	186	8.8	26.7
Melanoma skin	163	6.6	23.7	Lung	132	6.2	19.0
Rectum and RS jt				Rectum and RS jt			
and anal canal	142	5.7	20.6	and anal canal	105	5.0	15.1
Bladder	120	4.8	17.4	Corpus uteri	102	4.8	14.6
Stomach	112	4.5	16.2	Lymphomas	93	4.4	13.3
Lymphomas	110	4.4	15.9	Cervix	82	3.9	11.8
Lip	92	3.7	13.3	Ovary	76	3.6	10.9
Leukaemias	76	3.0	11.0	Pancreas	66	3.1	9.5
Kidney and ureters	73	2.9	10.6	Leukaemias	56	2.6	8.0
Pancreas	65	2.6	9.4	Stomach	54	2.5	7.7
Brain	52	2.1	7.5	Brain	38	1.8	5.4
				Kidney and ureters	35	1.6	5.0
				Bladder	28	1.3	4.0

*SA estimated population, ABS 1986

Table 5.4 Age-standardised cancer incidence per 100,000 population by calendar year*

Site	ICD-9	Sex	1977	1978	1979	1980	1981	1982	1983	1984	1985	1986	p Value
All sites	140-208	M	337.9	334.1	334.3	334.1	349.6	341.6	340.2	346.8	343.1	329.7	NS
		F	272.6	280.3	275.3	298.4	273.7	280.2	286.6	298.7	294.5	285.4	<0.05
Lip	140	M	11.4	11.6	7.9	9.3	12.5	12.7	16.7	16.3	16.5	12.5	<0.001
		F	0.7	2.1	1.6	1.7	2.9	3.8	3.2	4.8	3.2	4.0	<0.001
Stomach	151	M	16.8	16.5	15.9	17.6	16.8	14.9	18.8	15.1	16.7	15.0	NS
		F	9.5	10.3	10.7	11.3	7.4	9.6	7.6	7.7	6.2	7.0	<0.001
Small intestine (including duodenum)	152	M	1.5	1.0	1.0	0.6	0.5	0.7	0.3	0.4	1.1	0.8	NS
		F	0.8	0.5	0.6	0.8	0.6	0.1	1.3	1.2	1.5	0.3	NS
Colon	153	M	24.5	25.2	29.0	27.1	31.0	25.6	30.4	27.2	26.6	29.3	NS
		F	31.6	33.2	29.1	32.1	30.1	30.5	27.3	32.0	31.7	28.5	NS
Rectum etc	154	M	16.2	16.9	16.6	20.0	24.0	21.4	19.8	21.7	22.8	19.2	<0.01
		F	13.4	14.4	11.7	12.9	11.9	19.2	13.0	14.5	13.4	14.2	NS
Pancreas	157	M	11.1	9.4	9.7	7.4	9.8	11.5	8.3	7.2	7.7	8.8	<0.05
		F	9.0	6.7	9.1	5.7	6.3	6.6	7.9	4.7	6.6	8.7	NS
Larynx	161	M	5.8	5.6	5.4	4.2	6.4	6.0	7.5	6.3	6.5	5.8	NS
		F	0	0.6	0.7	0.8	1.2	0.9	1.4	0.7	0.5	0.1	NS
Lung etc	162	M	65.9	64.2	68.5	64.1	61.7	59.5	63.5	58.8	53.5	53.5	<0.001
		F	11.3	11.7	12.0	15.6	16.4	14.3	14.0	17.2	14.1	18.0	<0.001
Melanoma of skin	172	M	15.6	17.9	13.7	14.7	14.7	17.9	17.0	17.9	22.6	22.1	<0.001
		F	20.9	20.9	20.7	17.9	21.5	17.6	21.7	22.2	26.2	25.6	<0.01
Female breast	174	M	-	-	-	-	-	-	-	-	-	-	-
		F	67.2	70.7	66.3	77.1	62.0	68.8	70.1	68.3	75.3	69.8	NS

Table 5.4   Age-standardised cancer incidence per 100,000 population by calendar year* continued

Site	ICD-9	Sex	1977	1978	1979	1980	1981	1982	1983	1984	1985	1986	p Value
Cervix (invasive)	180	M	–	–	–	–	–	–	–	–	–	–	–
		F	9.5	12.1	10.6	12.0	10.7	9.0	12.5	12.3	12.5	11.2	NS
Uterus body	182	M	–	–	–	–	–	–	–	–	–	–	–
		F	20.8	14.8	16.6	17.1	13.4	13.3	15.3	17.2	15.2	14.1	<0.05
Ovary etc	183	M	–	–	–	–	–	–	–	–	–	–	–
		F	12.8	10.6	11.0	11.4	11.7	8.3	12.0	10.9	11.3	10.4	NS
Vagina, vulva etc	184	M	–	–	–	–	–	–	–	–	–	–	–
		F	2.5	2.8	2.4	4.0	2.4	2.3	2.7	3.1	2.5	2.4	NS
Prostrate	185	M	51.3	53.5	52.8	50.7	56.1	56.1	53.5	54.8	56.5	51.7	NS
		F	–	–	–	–	–	–	–	–	–	–	–
Kidney	189	M	8.8	10.6	9.7	8.6	9.9	8.2	9.1	10.5	8.8	9.9	NS
		F	3.0	5.3	5.2	6.5	5.7	5.3	6.2	6.6	4.8	4.6	NS
Brain	191	M	8.5	6.1	6.9	8.1	8.7	8.7	8.4	5.9	8.3	7.3	NS
		F	5.8	4.6	4.5	5.4	6.9	4.7	5.6	4.7	5.5	5.3	NS
Lymphomas	200-202	M	13.6	13.5	16.4	14.8	13.1	18.7	13.7	18.5	13.9	14.7	NS
		F	9.9	14.0	15.6	13.2	12.5	10.4	10.9	13.0	11.3	12.4	NS
Multiple myeloma etc	203	M	6.0	4.7	5.2	3.8	4.9	3.6	3.9	4.6	3.1	3.0	<0.01
		F	3.3	2.9	4.2	3.8	3.3	4.2	2.9	3.4	3.1	4.1	NS
Leukaemias	204-208	M	11.0	13.6	9.8	13.6	11.3	12.8	11.1	12.8	12.7	10.3	NS
		F	8.4	6.5	7.5	10.1	8.1	8.1	6.8	8.3	9.6	7.5	NS

*Standardised directly using the estimated South Australian population for 30 June 1981.
NS Not statistically significant (p>0.05).

The hospital's response

Prevention

Patients are only permitted to smoke if they have a prescription from their doctor; in practice, this has restricted smoking to a small number of psychiatric and terminally-ill patients. Visitors are not allowed to smoke in the hospital, nor staff while on duty. These measures have had a remarkable effect on the hospital environment and on patient and staff attitudes, and are in line with the aim to reduce smoking in the community by half by the year 2000.

The hospital has an active health promotion unit which serves patients and staff. Specific help with dietary advice, stop smoking programmes, and stress education are offered to all outpatients and inpatients by referral.

Diagnosis – early detection

Colorectal cancer is the commonest form of cancer in our community, accounting for nearly 500 cases per million population each year. No primary preventive strategy is available, and the only effective treatment is surgery; radiotherapy and chemotherapy do not appear to affect outcome. The five-year survival rate is just under 50 per cent and has not changed significantly in 30 years; the success of surgical treatment is dependent on removing the tumour before the invasion phase.

The Institute of Medical and Veterinary Science has developed a polyclonal antibody to human haemoglobin which can be used to screen for blood in the faeces. This test is not affected by diet and so is far superior to available chemical tests; it has been shown to be more sensitive and specific than other immunochemical tests. It is available as a diagnostic test and will be available as a screening test for colorectal cancer, offered annually to everyone over 40.

Screening for *cervical cancer* is readily available in Australia, but poorly controlled and organised and thought not to be effective. Cervical cancer incidence has increased over the past four years due, it is thought, to the papilloma virus being a sexually transmitted disease. Although general education is important, it is thought that cervical cytology screening is more likely to be effective than primary prevention. The Institute of Medical and Veterinary Science, which already provides the largest public cervical cytology service in the state, is to provide a new statewide service, backed by epidemiological information and general practitioner communication.

The aetiology of *breast cancer*, which accounts for one in every four cancers in women, is poorly understood; a primary preventive strategy is therefore difficult. Screening mammography backed by fine needle cytology and modern surgical treatment has been shown to reduce mortality from this cancer substantially. The cost of screening all women over 50 in Australia is estimated at $124m a year, so this is not practical. But it is intended to screen women with a high risk, and the Royal Adelaide Hospital has established a comprehensive screening and treatment team along with new radiology and pathology diagnostic facilities.

Treatment

Even if these preventive measures are effective, programmes may take between 20 and 30 years to affect the community cancer toll. (If everybody stopped smoking tomorrow for instance, it would take between 12 and 20 years for lung cancer to reduce by about 85 per cent of today's levels.) So it is essential to plan cancer treatment services with the objectives of cure, remission and palliation.

In 1977, treatment of cancer at the Royal Adelaide Hospital focused on the site of appearance of the neoplasm in the body. Treatment was the concern of organ or system specialists, and this tended to obscure the fundamental principles of growth disorder common to many varieties of tumour. It is now recognised that neoplasis is a multidisciplinary treatment problem requiring the collaboration of many specialists, including physicians, surgeons, radiotherapists, medical oncologists, pathologists, immunologists and epidemiologists. The problem also requires the expertise of people such as specialists, nurses, radiographers and counsellors. In addition, many patients receive more than one type of treatment for cancer. Half the new patients receive surgery, 40 per cent radiotherapy and 30 per cent chemotherapy.

After a series of papers and discussions, the Royal Adelaide Hospital is changing from providing individual patient care by a personal physician to providing care within a comprehensive cancer care centre.

Comprehensive cancer care centre

This is a multidisciplinary approach to the treatment of cancer, consisting of the services of radiation oncology, medical oncology and surgical oncology, with a wide range of support from associated disciplines. Services include a cancer registry, rehabilitation, social welfare, convalescent and intermediate care, home care support, patient follow-up and public education.

A centre of this sort, devoted to diagnosis and treatment of cancer patients, basic and clinical cancer research and the training of personnel, is essential. The patterns of care studies in the United States have conclusively demonstrated a significant improvement in patient morbidity and mortality by comprehensive cancer centres compared with limited modality cancer treatment centres. The standard and quality of equipment and drugs are among the many reasons for this.

Accordingly, an oncology committee has been established at the Royal Adelaide Hospital. This committee of the board, representing all the main services as well as ancillary services, has produced six major changes.

Tumour clinics Newly-diagnosed cases of cancer are presented to multidisciplinary tumour clinics which advise the treating practitioner and the patient. We consider this a major advance on the previous situation, in which a wide range of treatments was given to patients for the same cancer. There are clinics for leukaemia and lymphoma, for cancers of breast, head and neck, lung and brain, and for gynaecological and colorectal cancers. Urology and skin clinics are being established.

Treatment protocol After review of the international literature by interested groups, recommended treatment guidelines have been published. All medical staff are expected to adhere to these or to justify variations to the relevant tumour clinic.

Chemotherapy treatment centres The hospital has developed an oncology day centre as well as nominating a limited number of inpatient services for the delivery of chemotherapy. This policy has had the desired effect of eliminating one-off or non-approved therapeutic regimens through peer review. It has also been essential, for staff occupational health and safety reasons, to prepare cytotoxic drugs aseptically and centrally and to provide for 'closed' administration to patients.

Radiotherapy There has been a review of this therapy and essential training for doctors, physicists and radiographers. Linear accelerators only are used for curative treatment, in the knowledge that other forms of radiation treatment are inferior. Emphasis on planning and simulation have been necessary to produce better treatment results and reduce complications. The change to multiple field treatment to improve cure rate and reduce side effects has been important; so has computerised CT planning of treatments.

Hospital-based cancer registry The formal establishment of this type of surveillance has been important in evaluating treatment outcomes. Treatment results within the hospital are compared with international results and publicly released. We have been able to identify changes in approach to cancer treatment over time.

Equipment and staffing policies   The need for staff and equipment for a comprehensive cancer care centre has been assessed. This has had major financial implications which have required the redeployment of resources away from other areas of the hospital; it has also raised internal difficulties in the use of resources in cancer treatment.

National standards for cancer services

The hospital was concerned at the variation in standards and provision of services for cancer in Australia, and was asked to assist in the preparation of national guidelines. The following recommendations from its committee have been adopted by the ministers of health for Australia, the States and Territories:

1. *Organisation*   Major cancer treatment services should be provided by a comprehensive cancer service associated with a teaching hospital and ideally serving a catchment population of 1 million.

2. *Coordination*   One medical practitioner should be responsible for the overall care of the patient, and for the coordination of multidisciplinary treatments.

3. *Patient care*   The social, emotional and welfare aspects of both therapeutic and palliative care are best served by a team associated with a comprehensive cancer service.

4. *Bed/population ratios*   The recommended bed provision for combined chemotherapy, radiotherapy and haematological cancer units is 70 inpatient beds, 20 day beds and 20 hostel beds per million catchment population.

5. *Staff/population ratios*   The recommended full-time equivalent specialist medical staffing per million population is seven radiotherapists and four medical oncologists.

6. *Referral*   Referrals should flow to designated cancer services. In cancers with a low incidence, treatment specialisation should be undertaken by specified states and referral/consulting services formalised.

7. *Transport and accommodation*   Planning of cancer services, especially for less populated areas, should explicitly include transport and accommodation requirements.

8. *Paediatric cancer services*   The recommended whole-time equi-

valent specialist medical staffing per three million population is two paediatric oncologists (one with a special interest in haematology) and one visiting radiotherapist with a special interest in paediatric oncology. Beds should be provided within paediatric departments.

9. *Prevention*   Governments should establish objectives for the prevention of cancer and fund or otherwise promote preventive programmes.

10. *Screening and early detection*   Governments should establish objectives for early detection of cancer and for screening of high risk groups.

11. *Research*   Governments should initiate or otherwise support research into causative factors in cancer and into evaluating cancer treatment services.

12. *Information services and evaluation*   A cancer data base should be developed (at the national, state and hospital level) with the specific objective of providing data which can be used for:

   epidemiological studies of incidence, prevalence and survival in the community;

   evaluating cancer treatment services, especially cost effectiveness and evaluation of new technologies;

   planning future treatment services.

13. *Training and education*   Facilities for training radiation and medical oncologists, radiation physicists, nurses and radiographers should be regularly accredited by the appropriate professional body. Education about cancer prevention and cancer treatment should be provided for medical and other health practitioners at the undergraduate level. Continuing education to update knowledge and skills should also be provided.

14. *Safety*   The side effects of surgery, radiation and drug treatments and the working conditions of staff should be monitored with a view to reducing dangerous practices. In particular, formal radiation safety and control programmes, and standards for handling dangerous therapeutic substances should be adopted in all centres offering cancer treatment services.

15. *Access*   Patient education, referral and provision of radiotherapy treatment should be planned to overcome the present disparities between the States and Territories and to ensure access to treatment for those living in non-metropolitan areas.

CONSIDERING EFFICIENCY
AND ECONOMY

Organising health in New Zealand
Connecting summary

	Assessment of health needs	Formulation of objectives and priorities for intervention	Development and operation of programmes	Assessment of impact
Access				
Relevance to needs				
Effectiveness				
Equity				
Social acceptability				
Efficiency and economy	░░░	░░░		

The people of New Zealand are having similar experiences to those of many other countries. To George Salmond, it feels as if they have awakened after a long period of complacency to find that money is short and that, as a nation, they have invested badly in their health care system. The expansion of hospitals has been to the disadvantage of public health and community care. And as the population gets older and lives longer, more and more people feel this disadvantage. Unfortunately there are no silent benefactors to enable the people and their health care system to live happily ever after. Hard decisions about the allocation and management of limited resources become urgent.

This case study of New Zealand's attempt to gain control of an out-of-control health care system may feel familiar to many. Another familiar experience is the appointment of a firm of consultants from outside health care to make a hard-hitting report about the dearth of workable management and information systems. One of their main recommendations for making major savings was a restructuring of management. Notably, they recommend that there should be a separation between providers and funders.

I have plotted the dilemmas and responses highlighted by Salmond along the quality dimensions of efficiency and economy. I felt that his description paid attention to the first two building blocks: assessment of need and formulating objectives and priorities for intervention. The demand for swift changes raises many questions about what to make a priority and what to act on at which level. What does the reader predict would be the impact on health result?

6

ORGANISING HEALTH IN NEW ZEALAND

George Salmond

This paper traces the development of health services in New Zealand and focuses particularly on developments since 1984, initiated by the third Labour government. It asks whether it is necessary in New Zealand to separate organisationally the funders and providers of care.

Background to change

Over the last 50 years, health status and health services development in New Zealand have closely paralleled the country's social and economic development. Long before the election of the first Labour government in 1935, there had been a growing feeling that medical care and health services should be more widely available, irrespective of ability to pay. In April 1938, the government moved to introduce social security legislation which sought, among other things, to provide universal medical and hospital care for all, financed entirely out of tax revenue.

Inpatient and outpatient care, free at the point of delivery in a public hospital, were introduced without difficulty. There was, however, protracted conflict between the government and the medical profession over the payment of medical practitioners. In November 1941, a compromise was reached whereby a 'fee-for-service' scheme was introduced for ambulatory care.

After the second world war, the New Zealand economy boomed and the hospital service in particular benefited greatly. The public hospital was easily found in any town by looking for a construction crane. The weight of public expenditure moved progressively in favour of hospitals, to the disadvantage of public health and community care. By the early 1970s, over 70 per cent of health expenditure went on hospitals – which is high by international standards.

The 'fee-for-service' scheme meant that general practitioners had initially done well. But inflation was allowed to erode the government contribution, and co-payment increased. Today, only about a third of the cost of general practitioner care is met by the state, the rest being co-paid by the patient. This has been one factor in the recent rapid growth of health insurance.

By 1960, New Zealand's economic fortunes had started to wane. Between 1961 and 1980 absolute per capita GDP deteriorated sharply; New Zealand fell from sixth among OECD countries at the start of the period to eighteenth at the end. Health status indicators continued to improve, but declined in relation to those of other OECD countries, in parallel with relatively poor economic performance. Growth in the health system continued at about 5 per cent a year in real terms until the mid-1970s, with practically no real growth since 1980.

During the years of relative affluence, New Zealanders were complacent about their lifestyle and place in the world, and this complacency was certainly evident in the health services. Responsibility for the booming hospital service was vested in locally elected hospital boards; there were 29 by 1980, serving populations ranging in size from 2,500 to 800,000. Capital and operating finance were still provided by the central government out of general revenue. A trio of officers – a medical practitioner, a nurse and an administrator – managed the affairs of the board by consensus. There was no chief executive in the general management sense. The main management task was to expand the existing service in accord with the growth monies available.

Managing for health result: developments since 1984

The third Labour government was elected in July 1984 and immediately set about restructuring the economy. Government trading departments, such as the Post Office, Electricity Department, Railways and Forest Service, were made competitively neutral and transformed into state-owned enterprises, and the government embarked on a programme to sell off state assets to private enterprise. It also planned to introduce a single tax rate of less than 30 per cent, to enhance New Zealand's international competitiveness and to encourage individual and collective productivity gains.

In this environment, government spending on social services must come under increasing pressure. In late 1986, the government set up a Royal Commission on Social Policy to report in less than two years 'on what fundamental or significant reformation or changes are necessary or desirable in existing policies, administration, institutions or systems to secure a more fair, humanitarian, consistent, efficient and economic social policy which will meet the changed and changing needs of this country and achieve a more just society'.

There is a strong and growing consensus among New Zealanders that central government is too closely involved in their daily lives. This is particularly so in social policy areas, including health.

There is already commitment to major reform of local government, which could see a greater devolution of powers and functions to a relatively small number of large regional authorities. In the health sector, moves are under way to create a network of area health boards which combine public hospital functions with the public health function of district offices of the Department of Health. Financial, personnel and administrative functions, as well as service ones, will be devolved to the boards.

In 1986, the government commissioned a review of health benefits – state-financed subsidies designed to reduce financial barriers to health care.[1] Following that review, the government reaffirmed its commitment to the continued predominance of public funding and provision of health care, and gave notice of its intention to devolve the administration of health benefits – including the 'fee-for-service' payments to general practitioners – to area health boards.

Foreshadowing these developments, the Department of Health moved to restructure its operation with the aim of making the organisation more responsive to the changing environment. The progressive introduction of general management structures and processes across the whole organisation was pivotal to these changes. In place of systems based on shared and often ill-defined responsibilities and accountabilities, unit and programme managers were appointed to take direct responsibility for performance against clear objectives.

Concern continued about the level of public spending on health and the efficiency with which resources were used. In early 1987 the Ministers of Finance and Health set up a Taskforce to report on the efficiency of the public hospital sector. The chairman, Mr Alan Gibbs, was a highly successful businessman who was closely involved in the formation of state-owned enterprises.

The Taskforce engaged a firm of overseas consultants to make a performance assessment of the public hospital system. In a hard-hitting report, the consultants highlighted the dearth of management information, particularly on the cost of services. Major savings, they said, could be made by introducing more ambulatory care and reducing the length of hospital stay. In total, they estimated, over $600m could be saved on a 1986/7 expenditure base of $1,858m – a saving of over 30 per cent.[2]

Before the Taskforce reported, however, the government introduced a State Sector Bill which sought fundamentally to change personnel and industrial arrangements for the public service and other parts of the state sector – including hospitals and area health boards. After a stormy passage, the bill became law in April 1988.

The State Sector Act requires a fundamental reform of the management culture and clears the way for general management structures and systems across the health services. Chief executives on individual contracts for up to five years will be appointed to head government departments, each responsible to their minister. The State Services Commission will continue to negotiate for conditions of employment in the public service, but will be required to consult with the chief executives, who will have greater direct control over their employees than was the case previously.

The act requires that area health and hospital boards also appoint general managers on contract, who will then become the employers. In consultation with general managers and the Chief Executive of the Ministry of Health, the State Services Commission will negotiate conditions of employment for all board employees, but is expected to delegate most of these powers to the general managers in time.

The dilemma

The Taskforce on hospital and related services reported early in 1988 and, as expected, was roundly critical of many aspects of hospital performance. It proposed a structure which retained government as the main funder and provider of services, but which clearly separated these two roles. This separation, it said, would enable a market to be created in which prices were set by modified competition between hospitals. 'Thus the best performers will have an influence which will pervade the system over time even though they may never be a direct "competitor" with more distant hospitals'.[3]

The Taskforce's system would see central government funding directed on a population basis to six locally elected regional health authorities, which would then purchase publicly-funded health services on behalf of the people in the region. They would not manage or own any services, but would contract with public, private and voluntary providers on a competitively neutral basis. Central to the recommendations is the assertion that 'no major improvement in our system can be achieved without paying hospitals and other providers for the specific treatments they provide'.

So the Taskforce believed that the required efficiencies would be achieved only with a clear separation between funding and providing functions. Herein lies the dilemma.

After more than a decade of talk and little action, health sector reform has now come with a rush. The creation of area health boards and regionalised services is well under way. Long-standing problems about the future of health benefits look like being resolved by devolution to area health boards. The Department of Health has been restructured in keeping with its new function as a Ministry. The 1988

State Sector Act has cleared the way for reshaping the management culture of the health system and bold initiatives are under way to improve information systems and management performance. There is also the dimension of biculturalism (see Building new partnerships with the Maori people, page 138). Given all these changes and the inevitable uncertainty and confusion, at least in the short term, do we need to take the added step of separating funders and providers?

The Minister of Finance initially favoured the Taskforce's proposals, while the Health Minister was more cautious. The area health and hospital boards, smarting under the Taskforce's criticisms were generally against the proposals. The health worker unions roundly rejected them. The general public, as evidenced by reporting in the news media, were not greatly interested, tending to agree with the Taskforce's criticisms, but less certain about what should be done.

Finally, the government rejected the Taskforce's main recommendation. In October 1988, the then Minister of Health published a prescription for change in the health sector, based on:

continuing a publicly-funded health service;

a small Ministry of Health with policy review and support functions;

a network of 14–16 area health boards with largely elected members and an elected chairman;

a National Health Council consisting of the Minister and representatives of the Ministry and area health boards, to oversee national policy development;

improved information and management systems;

greater accountability of boards, both locally and to central government;

eventual devolution of all primary care services to health boards.

In December 1988, a new Minister of Health took on the portfolio. During the following three months, social policy spending came under extreme pressure, with budget re-cuts of between six and ten per cent in real terms for area health and hospital boards for the year 1989/90. Under these new pressures, and on top of other long-standing problems, the Auckland Area Health Board, the largest in the country, became financially insolvent and was replaced by a commission.

The Auckland experience confirmed in the mind of the Minister, Helen Clark, that boards were under-managed and largely incapable of reallocating resources in times of financial hardship. She continued with the establishment of area health boards, but sought to make these more directly accountable to central government for the resources they use. Work started on a national health charter as the basis for individual board contracts, which would prescribe in some detail the quantity and quality of services to be provided. The Ministry of Health was asked to develop review procedures which would ensure that boards met their contract obligations.

The Minister also legislated to enable her to appoint five members of each area health board, so reducing the number of elected members. She indicated that the planned devolution of primary care benefits would not go ahead until the new charter and accountability mechanisms were in place and managerial performance had markedly improved. In sum, she moved to put in place a much more centrally-driven system for health sector management.

References

1. Scott, C, Fougere, G and Marwick, J. Choices for health care: report of the health benefits review. Wellington, Government Printer, 1987.

2. Arthur Anderson and Co. Public hospital performance: report to the New Zealand Department of Health, September 1987.

3. Gibbs, A G, Fraser, D R and Scott, P J. Unshackling the hospitals: report of the hospital and related services taskforce. Wellington, Government Printer, 1988.

Management reform in a London hospital
Connecting summary

	Assessment of health needs	Formulation of objectives and priorities for intervention	Development and operation of programmes	Assessment of impact
Access				
Relevance to needs				
Effectiveness				
Equity				
Social acceptability				
Efficiency and economy		▨	▨	

People do not much like change. They prefer the familiar, which is less threatening than the unknown. Yet change happens.

Cyril Chantler's case study of management reform in a London teaching hospital discusses the difficult experience of a deteriorating relationship between administration and doctors. Guy's Hospital had other problems too: it has the dubious distinction of being the first London teaching hospital to have spent more money by closing beds.

Not surprisingly, the hospital responded to its financial crisis by tightening up on the efficiency and economy dimension of quality, and that is the dimension along which I have plotted this case study. It seems, too, that the hospital's initial response was to go straight into setting priorities and objectives and putting operational plans in motion, perhaps at the expense of an assessment of needs. This response assumed a knowledge both of people's needs and of the impact of their efforts. What predictions does the reader have about how the hospital will be able to respond when providers and purchasers of health care are separated?

MANAGEMENT REFORM IN A
LONDON HOSPITAL

Cyril Chantler

This case history analyses the experience at Guy's Hospital between 1985 and 1988, during which time major management changes were introduced. It analyses why the changes were thought necessary and the philosophy behind them and draws out some lessons for others. These include principles and systems that minimise conflict and confusion.

Guy's Hospital opened in 1726 in Southwark, a densely populated area which was then, and is now, one of considerable deprivation. The first purpose of the hospital is to serve the local population; it is also a major teaching hospital which qualifies over 100 doctors, 90 dentists and a large number of nurses and people in allied health professions each year. The hospital is next to a very busy railway station which provides transport into London to a population of over 3.5 million. The catchment population of Guy's is, therefore, much larger than its local one. It also has an important role in the provision of tertiary referral services as well as in postgraduate teaching and research.

Background to change: Guy's and the NHS 1948–85

Guy's was incorporated into the National Health Service in 1948. The board of governors had overall responsibility for its management, reporting to the Minister of Health. Overall responsibility for the administration of the hospital rested with the clerk to the governors: this post was considered one of the most senior in hospital administration in the country. Day-to-day responsibility for running the hospital was vested in the superintendent, who was always a clinician and responsible to the board. In effect, he shared total responsibility along with the clerk and the matron.

In retrospect, 1948–1974 were 'the years of plenty' and saw a steady expansion in Guy's services. The NHS provided the money to run the hospital, but the board of governors had access to the trust funds of Thomas Guy, which were used for new developments. Although the hospital tried to stay within its financial allocation, it was not in effect cash limited and legitimate demands for increased services could always be funded with the allocation adjusted at the end of each year; the government took over responsibility for items funded the previous year by the governors. In 1948, the board assumed responsibility for a nearby children's hospital with 100 beds, and later for St Olave's and New Cross hospitals, both about two miles from Guy's. So by 1974, the Guy's group had access to a total of 1,557 beds, 887 of which were on the main site.

In 1974, the board of governors was abolished. The community health and hospital services were joined into the Guy's health district, which with three other districts formed an area health authority. The post of superintendent at Guy's was abolished and the district management team was set up, with the chairman of the medical and dental staff committee, a general practitioner, district treasurer, district administrator and district nursing officer working by consensus. The post of district administrator was far less senior in career terms than the previous post of clerk to the governors and the consensus management model was totally different from the old pattern of responsibilities. Finally, instead of Guy's reporting directly to the Minister of Health, the reporting structure now went through area to region to the Department of Health and Social Security.

In 1976, the then Labour government introduced the concept of cash limits on public expenditure, which were strictly applied by the subsequent Conservative government in 1979. Area health authorities were obliged not to overspend, and expense in the health service, having been to some extent demand-led, became strictly limited by the cash allocation. Inevitably, this led to overspending and the financial position of both Guy's and the area health authority rapidly deteriorated.

In 1978, considerable cutbacks in clinical services were proposed, with an overall reduction at Guy's of 30 per cent. The clinicians produced an alternative plan to close St Olave's hospital, with a resulting 10 per cent reduction in clinical services. This policy was eventually adopted, but only after the government had replaced the area health authority with commissioners. In the end, the necessary financial savings were made.

In 1982, a further reoganisation of the NHS abolished the area health authorities. The Guy's and Lewisham health districts were joined as the Lewisham and North Southwark Health Authority, reporting to the South East Thames Regional Health Authority. The district was split into three units of management: Guy's Hospital, Lewisham Hospital and the Priority Community Care Services. Overall responsibility was held by the district management team which reported to the district health authority which was made up of

75

people representing various local interests and headed by a chairman appointed by the Secretary of State.

The new health authority decided on a radical plan to improve the provision of health care in the community and, in particular, to close long-stay mental handicap hospitals and rehouse their patients in small groups in the community. They determined to obtain money for this plan by reducing expenditure in Guy's and Lewisham hospitals. The regional health authority also decided to reduce allocation to our health authority by £12m a year at current price over a 10 year period (10 per cent of allocation). Other cuts, such as inflation shortfall and planned efficiency savings, mean that between 1982/3 and 1987/88 the Guy's district suffered a loss of £12,430,000 a year. Guy's Hospital budget fell by £10,235,000 in the five years 1982–87, leaving a budget of about £50m a year.

In January 1984 it was apparent that the hospital was going to overspend its allocation substantially, and the then district management team decided to close over 100 beds, although a number of clinicians suggested that the effect would not be as foreseen. During the next two months, throughput in the hospital increased over that in the same two months the previous year. Guy's thus had the dubious distinction of being the first London hospital to spend more money by closing beds.

The combination of increased demand for our services, and reduction in our allocation, beds and other clinical services, led to a crisis of management within the hospital. Relationships deteriorated rapidly between different professional groups, not least the clinicians and the administrators. The administrators felt that the advice they were getting from the medical advisory committee (based on a divisional cogwheel representational system) was irresponsible, because it took no account of the financial problems. The clinicians felt that the administrators had lost their vision of the aims of the hospital – that is, to care for the sick. Tensions were apparent at all levels: on the wards when doctors wished to admit patients to beds which were undernursed because of reductions in the nursing service; within the nursing heirarchy, with their long lines of communication imposed by the Salmon structure; and between different professional groups who sought to protect their particular service.

At this time the Griffiths report was published.[1] Clinicians and others at Guy's had already had discussions with the Griffiths team, suggesting that clinicians should be involved in the management of the hospital with their own budgets related to their clinical services, and with decentralisation of services as far as practical.

This then was the background to the debate on a new management structure.

Managing for change: do doctors have a role?

It is often argued that clinicians should not actively participate in hospital management because of a possible conflict of interest between the allocation of resources and the needs of their own patients.[2] Failure to recognise this dilemma may compromise the primary duty of doctor to patient or lead to resource allocations which are unfair to those whose needs are less acute or who are represented by less persuasive doctors. Clinical freedom is obviously, however, constrained by lack of resources, and if that freedom is to be maximised, it is important for clinicians to have a voice in the debate on resource allocation.

The medical advisory committee system worked well when the service was expanding, and works well in a private hospital where doctors are, in effect, customers of the institution because they introduce the patients who in turn pay the bills. But in a cash-limited system, the position is different. No authority charged with maintaining financial stability will transfer responsibility for expenditure to any other group, unless that group accepts the financial constraints within which they have to operate.

All consultants in the NHS have equal status and the possibility that any one of them should have authority over others is properly resisted. Clinicians contemplating involvement in hospital management are also concerned about the time it will take and fear that their clinical activities will be limited.

Professional health service administrators and managers tend to have mixed feelings about the involvement of clinicians in management. They are concerned that clinicians commit the resources, leaving the administrators to cope with the financial and organisational consequences. They also feel that many clinicians know little about the complexity of delivering health care and so tend to make irrational and uninformed decisions. But administrators also recognise that clinicians are directly involved with the customer; tend to be semi-permanent in the organisation (whereas administrators move frequently as their career progresses); are intelligent and have stamina; and tend to be responsible for many service innovations.[3]

The balance of the argument, I believe, is in favour of involving clinicians. It helps to maximise their clinical freedom and to reduce the frustration of having only a limited influence on the service in which they work. It is also sensible to involve the most powerful professional group in the management of hospitals to increase the efficiency of the organisation. Certain principles and systems are necessary, however, to avoid conflict or confusion.

Principles and systems for management

1. *Professional and management accountability*

Hospitals are unusual in that they are staffed by professionals in a number of different fields, each of whom has their own well-developed professional structure, whether they are nurses, engineers, physicists, scientific officers or others. Clinicians are professionally accountable to their patients, and this accountability is audited by the traditions of Hypocrates, by various professional bodies, by the General Medical Council and by the law. Although NHS clinicians are paid by the government, their remuneration can legitimately be represented as coming from the patient through taxation.

Management accountability can legitimately be separated from professional accountability. Each member of staff has management accountability to the health authority for the quantity and quality of services delivered and for the efficiency of the work carried out. Any management structure must take account of the differences between professional and management accountability. Separate lines of accountability not only serve to maintain professional freedom but can also act as a useful check to the unrestrained use of authority.

2. *Responsibility and authority*

Responsibility and authority must be coterminous and commensurate. If a group of clinicians with a clinical director takes responsibility for providing a service, then the commensurate authority must be transferred to this individual. We need to recognise, though, the apprehension that some clinicians will feel about assuming responsibility for provision of service as opposed to individual patient care and the administration's resistance to transfer of authority.

3. *Management budgeting*

The NHS hospital service has traditionally operated on a functional budgeting system. This works well in hotel and support services, but has little relevance in the clinical service where it is clearly impossible for one person, such as the director of nursing, to be responsible for day-to-day nursing expenditure throughout the hospital.

The result of the cumbersome functional budgeting system is that there is little commitment accounting, little knowledge of day-to-day expenditure and little management control of expenditure. The actual amount spent in the service is only accurately known at the end of the financial year and quite often an over-expenditure is found when the final accounts are made; only then is it possible to deter-

78

mine exactly where the money went. This process is usually complete by mid-summer when the institution is well into its next financial year, so it is hardly surprising that hospital cuts tend to happen in the autumn.

It is fundamentally important, in my view, that the NHS adopt management budgeting throughout the service, so that all expenditure is under the control of named individuals who receive their budgets in advance and can check expenditure at regular intervals. Commitment accounting is an important component of such a system.

A decentralised clinical management structure needs to be served by a management (clinical) accountancy system. It is pointless to introduce clinical budgeting without a clinically-based management structure, because there is no point in having a budget if there is no one who accepts responsibility for it.

4. *Part-time clinical managers*

Clinicians must be allowed to be part-time managers and it should be recognised that their responsibility is for management and not for administration. If they have to devote a great deal of time to management, they will cease to be clinicians and their unique perspective will be lost. They need to be supported by able business managers, who may be drawn from the hospital administrative service or other professional groups. And they need to recognise that professional administrative skills are important. The emphasis is on a team approach and the basic team comprises the clinician, the business manager and the nurse manager.

The other important component in allowing clinicians to be part-time managers is decentralisation of the organisation. The work can then be shared among a number of clinicians, each of whom can commit a certain amount of time but not be overwhelmed by management responsibilities.

Managing change: Guy's Hospital 1985–88

In the autumn of 1984, the medical and dental committee, comprising all the consultants at Guy's, voted to take part in an experiment based on the above principles. A new hospital management board (board of directors) was formed and assumed responsibility for running the hospital in April 1985.

Management structure

The new management structure is shown in Figure 7.1. The chairman of the management board is ultimately responsible for the hospital's performance and reports directly to the district general manager and district health authority. The chairman works closely with the chief executive (who is responsible for the general management and overall objectives of the hospital) and with the director of nursing. These three individuals carry central responsibility for the hospital's performance. They are helped by a team made up of:

The clinical superintendent – responsible for medical staffing and hospital development (capital development costing over £30m is planned over five years). He or she also chairs the quality committee, which reports directly to the hospital management board.

The director of operations – responsible for hotel and support services.

The hospital finance director and staff.

The personnel director and staff.

Each of the 13 clinical directorates is headed by a clinician assisted by a nurse manager and a business manager. The latter were mainly chosen from among professional hospital administrators, but one is a nurse and another a scientific officer. Some directorates share a business manager and responsibility for the laboratories is shared between the director, the chief technician and a junior administration secretary.

The separation of management accountability from professional accountability is fundamental. The nurse-manager in a directorate reports directly to the director of nursing on professional matters, physicists report to the chief physician, and so on. Although these professional lines of accountability have not had to be invoked because of serious management difficulties, they exist if needed.

The chairman of the board is appointed by the district general manager but on advice from colleagues. If the chairman lost the support of either the board or of the Guy's medical and dental committee, then he or she would have little choice but to resign, irrespective of standing with the authority. The appointment of clinical directors has also been on advice from colleagues and with regard to their management capabilities as seen by the chairman of the board and the district general manager.

Figure 7.1   Guy's Hospital – management structure

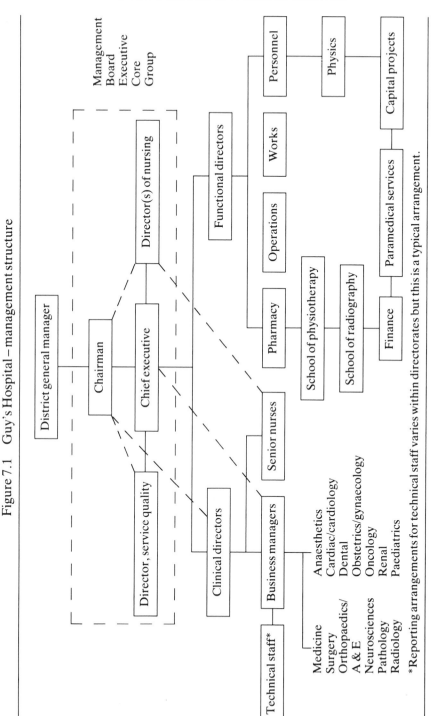

*Reporting arrangements for technical staff varies within directorates but this is a typical arrangement.

Decentralisation

By 1988, 1,828 out of a total staff of 2,916 reported within the decentralised directorates. Centralised outpatient appointing and management arrangements had been dismantled; these responsibilities are now assumed by their individual directorate for clinical firms. Admissions and the management of waiting lists have been largely decentralised to directorates, as have bed allocations, with as few clinical teams as possible working out of any one ward. Rules for bed borrowing have been established and only the director of admissions, who is also the director of the accident and emergency department, has the power to commandeer a bed. The authority of the ward sister or charge nurse over his or her ward has been re-established, and ward budgets, which they hold, have been introduced.

Management budgeting and finance

A management budgeting system, based on the model drawn up by consultants Arthur Young, has been introduced and applied to clinical budgeting. We are now able to capture expenditure on staffing costs, radiology and pharmacy, and these are contained within the budget negotiated each year with each directorate; pathology and medical/surgical supply and CSSD costs will be added. Budgets are negotiated between October and December and form an important component of the unit business plan presented to the board and the authority in March.

This budget review process is an important component of our system. It provides management appraisal where expenditure, and quantity and quality of activity are formally examined. Budget reviews can yield savings: £1,122,000 out of a total of £1,909,000 saved was reapplied to new developments in 1988/9, when the total budget was £51.574m.

The board inherited a deficit from 1984/5 of £1.2m and an inherent overspend in 1985/6 of over £300,000 a month. In August 1985, it was apparent that the unit was heading for an overspend in that financial year of over £5m – over 10 per cent of the budget. In order to contain this overspend, it was decided to concentrate on staff costs rather than, as previously, reducing clinical services. A strict manpower control system was therefore introduced. This took the place of a very loose control which had meant it was difficult to tell from month to month exactly how many people were employed in the hospital. Now total staffing was determined and individual managers, to whom staff reported, were identified. The number of posts was reduced by 300 (about 10 per cent) by the end of the financial year 1985/6, when the unit was overspent by £1.7m.

By the end of the following financial year, this deficit had been cleared and the unit was breaking even, as it was in 1987/8. The cuts have been severe. Since the beginning of 1984, Guy's has lost 2 per cent of its beds (340), manpower has been reduced by 17 per cent (575 posts) and expenditure by £7.8m a year (15 per cent).

Patient services

Despite the massive bed closures and financial reductions, inpatient throughput only fell to 6 per cent less than the 1982 maximum; in 1987/8 there were over 36,000 inpatient admissions, with further rises projected. There has been a considerable increase in efficiency, with length-of-stay and turnover interval declining sharply. An observation ward associated with the accident and emergency department takes the pressure off beds; there is a five-day ward and a day surgery unit. Waiting lists, which rose inexorably between 1982 and mid-1987, then started to decline quite sharply in most areas.

In 1985/6, Guy's was the most expensive London teaching hospital on patient-related cost per case; in 1986/7, it was eighth out of 11, and further improvements were expected. In 1986/7 we saw 69,754 new outpatients and the cost for each was the lowest of the three teaching hospitals in our area of London.

Quality issues

Quality of care is obviously important and we have not yet developed satisfactory outcome measures for this. We do know that our re-admission rate has not increased and our new system for planned discharges for the elderly and chronically disabled has a reporting system to judge inappropriate discharges. As far as we can tell, the quality of our care has not deteriorated.

The introduction of clinical audit throughout the hospital is also an urgent priority. The quality committee has introduced codes of practice for customer relations, such as outpatient waiting time, and these are being monitored.

The state of our buildings and medical and surgical equipment inventory is an important issue in quality. In 1984, the works officer estimated that there was a backlog of £12m on essential maintenance and we have begun to deal with this with a major lift refurbishment programme (£370,000 over three years initially), replacement of theatre cooling and air conditioning systems (£397,000), a new incinerator, relocation and refurnishing of the blood transfusion unit, and starting to improve the decorative state of the hospital and its roads and pavements.

The board has managed to protect and increase the works department budget. We have established an electrical and mechanical services unit and increased the budget for replacement of equipment. The quality committee and the board, with the clinical directors, are developing the introduction of management appraisal, definite guidelines for directorate responsibilities, a five-year plan of objectives for the hospital and new standards for communication.

Personnel issues

The massive reduction in staff obviously led to difficult personnel issues, but most redundancies were dealt with by natural wastage and only 42 compulsory redundancies were needed in a total of 576 posts lost. The majority of these posts came from the ancillary services, but the number of doctors and nurses had to be reduced as well. We are introducing a new system of private management for our domestic and portering staff, although they will remain as employees at Guy's.

Perhaps the most important positive change from our decentralised system has been the improvement in staff morale. Communications between different professional groups have improved, with much greater appreciation of everyone's essential contribution to the quantity and quality of health care. We have worked hard to achieve this; we have introduced a briefing system based on the monthly board meeting, which is followed by a newsletter to all managers for discussion with their staff, telling them of developments in the hospital.

The decentralisation of the records department staff to individual clinical teams has been particularly important. Recruitment has improved and turnover fallen dramatically. It is now relatively uncommon for a patient to attend without notes and x-rays which, three or four years ago, happened in as many as a third of attendances.

Resource management

Guy's has been appointed a second generation 'resource management' site as part of the national experiment by the NHS management board. As well as progressing with our clinical budgeting system, we are piloting a new personnel system and a nurse and theatre management system, all linked to a new patient administration system. We are also looking to develop case-mix analysis and the production of average cost-per-case data.

Conclusion

We believe that our approach to clinical management has much to commend it, certainly for this hospital. It confirms the success of a similar system in the Johns Hopkins Hospital in Baltimore, USA.[4] An exact facsimile of our model would not be widely applicable, but we would insist on certain principles. These relate particularly to the proper involvement of clinicians in management, the decentralisation of authority and responsibility and the development of team work between different professionals. While this paper has concentrated on the role of clinicians, the development of the management skills of business managers, and particularly nurse managers, has been an important part of our success so far.

References

1. Department of Health and Social Security. NHS management inquiry, Report (Leader of inquiry, Roy Griffiths). London, DHSS, 1983.

2. Chant, A D B. National Health Service: practising doctors should not manage. The Lancet, vol 1, no 8391, 1984, p 1398.

3. Stocking, B. Initiative and inertia: case studies in the NHS. Nuffield Provincial Hospitals Trust, 1985.

4. Heyssel, R M, Gaintner, J R, Kues, I W, Jones, A A and Lipstein, S H. Special report: decentralized management in a teaching hospital. New England Journal of Medicine, vol 310, no 22, 1984, pp 1477–80.

Shaping medical practices in Manitoba
Connecting summary

	Assessment of health needs	Formulation of objectives and priorities for intervention	Development and operation of programmes	Assessment of impact
Access				
Relevance to needs				
Effectiveness				
Equity				
Social acceptability				
Efficiency and economy				

'Medical staff increasingly face pressures that appear to limit their medical prerogatives, challenge their professional responsibilities and affect their earning power.'

There are new incentives to both doctors and administrators to liase more closely in the management of hospitals and health care. In Manitoba, one such incentive has been a policy to reduce the number of acute beds. The consequent change in the type of health care on offer requires a new set of relationships between 'stakeholders' to manage it.

Like Cyril Chantler, Dieter Kuntz describes his experiences in promoting these new relationships, and I have plotted his case study, like Chantler's, on the quality dimension of efficiency and economy and the two management building blocks, formulation of objectives and priorities for intervention and development and operation of programmes. Again, it seemed, the objectives had been based not on an assessment of need but on a response to financial constraints. Assessment of health needs, however, might be one of the next steps, as the consequences of the reforms become more evident and as, in Canada at least, consumers become more vocal. What does the reader think?

SHAPING MEDICAL PRACTICE
IN MANITOBA

Dieter Kuntz

Hospital organisations are extremely complex. The prime role of hospital management has been the organisational management of resources, with the goal of achieving effectiveness and efficiency in the provision of quality patient care. Traditionally, physicians have had considerable autonomy in the use of hospital resources. The hospital has been 'the doctors' workshop'. But cost containment incentives, together with a broader view of the hospital's governing board as ultimately responsible for the quality of care, have resulted in a crisis between the workshop and the doctor. Old relationships no longer hold.

This paper highlights the major forces that influence these changing relationships between administration and medical staff in Manitoba, Canada, and, more generally, in North America. It outlines one hospital's experience of assessing and resolving some difficult issues of medical staff organisation and practice. Although changes in these areas are likely to be perceived by doctors as a threat to their autonomy, it concludes, they are nevertheless likely to be less costly than those involving cuts and modifications in existing services.

Background to change

One of the main reasons for the complexity of hospitals is the day-to-day interaction between the governing board/administration and the organised medical staff. Their relationship has been unchanged since the evolution of community hospitals. Traditionally, in Manitoba, the physician could, on graduation, open a medical practice near the hospital and apply for privileges, with a right of appeal, should the institution deny the request, to such bodies as the Provincial Medical Appointments Review Committee. The physician could argue that the institution denied him or her the opportunity to practise his or her chosen profession, particularly if he or she was a specialist.

The governing board, usually made up of 'lay' people, is ultimately completely accountable for the quality of care. It delegates authority to the medical staff, who in turn discharge the responsibility through the medical staff by-laws, rules and regulations. This document has become the framework within which doctors can act with reasonable freedom and confidence. The medical staff traditionally determined the number of physicians on the hospital's staff and the types of privileges granted. Although board approval is required, this is usually seen as a rubber stamp. The impact on the institution is significant, since decisions on physician approval affect types of hospital services, patient mix and capital and operating costs.

The basis for the hospital/physician relationship is 'medical staff self-governance'. At the highest level, the board exercises its responsibility by reviewing and approving medical staff recommendations. The relationship between the two parties is one of inter-dependence. So what is the problem?

The problem is simply people. The stakeholders bring different perspectives, have different goals and protect different territory when treating the patient. In a telephone poll, 50 doctors and 50 hospital administrators were asked to say what they thought of each other.[1] Here are some results.

Hospital administrators said the doctors were:

egotistical bumblers, who resented and envied the administrators' organisational skills;

tinkerers who wanted to play with the most expensive and latest gadgetry;

above-average in some ways yet immature in interpersonal relations;

independent thinkers who unrealistically denied that in hospital they were part of an organisation;

confused about their responsibilities and authority in the hospital;

fundamentally unequipped to deal with non-medical matters.

Physicians said that hospital administrators were:

aloof, insecure bureaucrats;

more concerned with cost accounting than with patient care;

reluctant to ask for medical advice on cutting costs, staffing or allocation of space, while encroaching on issues that should be dealt with by the medical staff;

confused about authority and responsibility vis-a-vis medical staff;

always batting for the board and never for the doctors.

Physicians and administrators alike felt that the basic problem was a lack of effective communication, both in the organisation and between individuals.

The last decade has seen subtle changes in the roles of the governing board, administration and medical staff, and this has been uncomfortably recognised. The easy-going, non-interfering board members have been replaced by people who insist that hospitals must run like big businesses. Hard decisions are made in a commercial manner, taking into account such factors as growth, profit and the elimination of competition. Boards are now prepared to tackle bioethical issues, and service priorities, and are ever-mindful of the importance of an appropriate mix of medical staff to fulfill the organisation's mission.

The administrator used to manage day-to-day affairs for the medical staff and the board. The evolving role of the hospital's chief executive officer (CEO) reflects an institutional need for managerial leadership to meet the identified mission of a complex health industry, using such tools as affiliations, management contracts, acquisitions, mergers and development of health-related businesses.

Physicians were traditionally accustomed to viewing the hospital as their workshop. They are not necessarily pleased with certain changes. New medical staff are no longer elected by popular vote of the entire medical staff. Instead they are recommended to the board for appointment on the basis of their qualifications, and the board's decision is final. The security of life-long medical appointments has been replaced by reappointments every year or two. The nurses' relationships with management is closer than ever before and perhaps becoming even closer than that between physician and nurse. Medical staff by-laws have been revised to include obligations as well as privileges. Physicians are expected to use their clinical expertise to review and judge each other's clinical practice.

Medical staff increasingly face pressures that appear to limit their medical prerogatives, challenge their professional responsibility to provide appropriate medical care and affect their earning power. In the United States there is a movement, aimed at increasing medical staff autonomy, led by doctors committed to the concept of quality patient care. The leadership of the hospital medical staff section of the American Medical Association (AMA) has responded with a political strategy which aims to change the standards pertinent to medical staff of the Joint Commission on Accreditation of Healthcare Organisations (JCAHO). Various authorities believe it is time to re-examine medical staff and governing board standards. In 1985, the joint report of the American Medical Association and American Health Association (AHA) on hospital medical staff relations recognised the collective professional skills, knowledge and judgment of the organised medical staff and its delegated authority to accredit doctors and to carry out peer review and quality assurance. While the governing board is ultimately accountable and legally responsible for these functions, the independence given to the medical staff to fulfill them can be characterised as 'self-governing', which is not, for the AHA, synonymous with 'separation'.

The AHA advocates communication and consultation, not confrontation. This is evident in the revised language it has proposed to the JCAHO on unilateral amendments to medical staff by-laws:

'Amendments to medical staff by-laws are accomplished through a cooperative process involving both the medical staff and the governing body, and are effective upon approval by the governing body. Amendments are developed and adopted by the medical staff, or if initiated by the governing body, are submitted to the medical staff for consideration, adoption and/or recommendation to the governing body. The governing body gives full consideration to the recommendations and views of the medical staff before taking final action.'

It is no longer possible for individual hospitals to be 'the best at everything'. They must do a more rigorous job of environmental assessment, competitive analysis, organisational assessment and market analysis to determine those areas of comparative advantage where they should be striving for excellence. This needs to be done with the relevant involvement of medical staff. Assessments of their strengths, weaknesses and competitive advantages is the key to the development of effective relationships and the pursuit of responsible excellence. The challenge is for all parties to put aside their differences and identify mutually beneficial goals towards which to work as a team.

Improving medical staff relations: a hospital's experience

Victoria General Hospital in Winnipeg has 254 beds and was incorporated in 1911. It is primarily oriented towards surgery, with an above average number of specialists for a hospital of its size. The organisational structure (Figure 8.1) reflects the normal divisions into departments and medical staff committees. In the past few years, the hospital has experienced the pressures of cost containment, increased competition, changing technology and social and public expectations. In response to these pressures, the board administration and the medical staff felt the need to work more closely together.

Figure 8.1   Organisational chart of the Victoria General Hospital
medical staff, April 1987

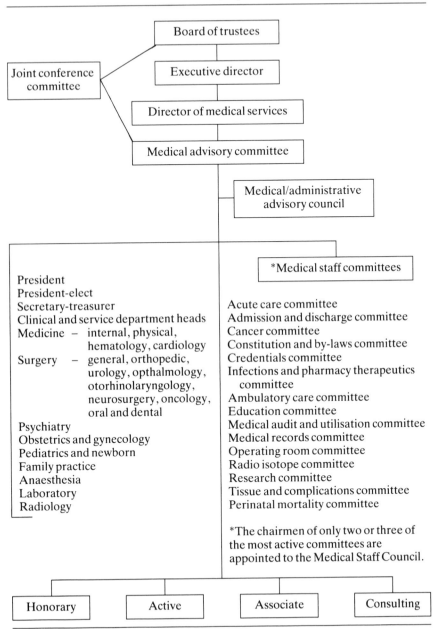

Present relationships

Victoria General Hospital enjoys good relationships with its professional staff. It is one of the few institutions where the president and president-elect of the medical staff are on the board, with voting privileges. (This decision does not have the support of the provincial government, although most Canadian provinces have legislation that requires a minimum of three staff physicians to have a voting place on the governing board. Our medical staff knew that our decision was not supported and was appreciative.) The board also invited a third member of the medical staff to participate on the finance committee; clinical input is needed to maintain the quality of care while making the most cost-effective decisions, particularly in the purchase of major equipment, and commitment to decisions is enhanced by participation in making them.

Meaningful medical staff by-laws, rules and regulations are essential. Boards can create an environment that eliminates 'we/they' friction and allows the medical staff the freedom to exercise collective professional judgment in matters relating to by-laws, credentials and quality assurance. At Victoria hospital, the medical staff has freedom to review and update its by-laws.

In the past ten years, the hospital has successfully put physicians on a fee retainer or salary, to the benefit of both doctors and institution. The hospital, for instance, employs ten medical house officers, who cover the emergency department for 24 hours a day, seven days a week. The anaesthetists charge a fee for service for elective surgery from Monday to Friday and provide 24 hour cover for a sessional fee for obstetrical intensive care and patient emergencies. Part-time positions, such as medical director of the intensive care unit and medical audit chairman, are paid retainers; pathologists are on a salary contract. A full-time paid medical director provides the day-to-day medical/administrative link.

(In the United States, the percentage of active staff physicians receiving some form of compensation from the hospital increased from 2.8 per cent in 1972 to 10.8 per cent a decade later. The number of hospitals which pay their chiefs of staff increased from 4.2 per cent to 7.6 per cent over the same period. In 1981, 15.7 per cent of hospitals reported having other salaried physicians.)

Improving relationships

In seeking a framework for avoiding, minimising and resolving differences, the major task was to bring the stakeholders together. We pursued two solutions: the medical/administrative advisory committee and the question of medical staff composition.

Medical/administrative advisory committee

This new committee reports to the medical advisory committee. Its members include six clinical heads (excluding radiology and laboratory) and the president of the medical staff; from the administrative side, it includes the executive director, director of medical services, associate executive director (patient care services), assistant executive directors (nursing and finance). The committee's first 18 months was revealing and helpful in promoting understanding of different perspectives within the team. Its multidisciplinary nature has been well received, even though it is considered a medical staff committee. It has addressed several major issues.

It has, for instance, researched the concept of a surgicentre modelled on the US experience. The government has endorsed a two-year demonstration project to show how, with appropriate community support, traditional inpatient surgery (such as hernia, haemorrhoids, vein ligations, plastic and orthopaedic surgery) can be successfully performed as outpatient operations. The committee has also been involved in setting up a laser centre which will, for instance, allow two-thirds of hysterectomies to be performed on outpatients; the department of surgery has insisted that new staff learn to use the equipment at their own expense.

The committee has tackled fiscal restraints and related issues. When Winnipeg's seven acute hospitals incurred a collective deficit of $23m in 1986/7, the government mandated them to balance their books for the following year. Our committee was charged with finding a reallocation of resources that was acceptable to board, administration and medical staff and its plan to close 15 surgical beds, at a saving of $400,000, was reluctantly endorsed. At another level, a programme has been designed, with the support of public health nurses, to reduce further the average obstetrical length of stay.

The committee is to be involved in long-term planning as well as short-term issues. For the first time, representatives of the medical staff are invited, through the medical/administrative advisory committee, to participate in the weekend retreat to review the hospital's long range plan. There is an evolution of medical ethics away from the Hippocratic tradition towards a business model of professional ethics.

The experience of the committee has been so positive that it is intended to include its terms of reference in the medical staff by-laws. It will then have equal stature and authority with other medical staff

Table 8.1   Financial impact for medical staff appointments
or new programs

1. Full name_____

2. Department_____

3. Specialty/section_____

4. Replacement (for whom) _____

5. Brief justification of the appointment or program_____

   _____

6. *Inpatient space, equipment and supplies:*

   – Estimated number of inpatient beds required_____

   – Estimated number of admissions/year_____

   – Average length of stay_____

   – Will there be a need for specialised equipment to support the inpatient beds?

     _____

   Cost: _____   _____   _____
             Initial   Maintenance   Estimated useful life

   – Will specialised supplies or drugs be required?_____
     Costs?_____

   – Will additional nursing or technical personnel be required?_____

   – Will existing personnel require additional training? Where?_____
     Cost?_____

7. – Estimated number of outpatient visits per year _____
     Will an outpatient clinic be required and who will staff it?_____

   – Will specialised equipment or staff be required for the outpatient clinic?_____

8. *Operating Room*

   Will OR time be required?_____

   _____ inpatient   _____ ASU

   Estimated number of surgical procedures/year

       (a)
       (b)
       (c)

   Will this require additional OR staff or additional training for existing staff?
   Where can such staff be trained and what will be the cost?

   Estimated number of such patients who will require a ventilator and/or
   ICU postoperatively?_____

committees. It is important that the rest of the medical staff perceives that they have the opportunity to influence policy decisions and the direction of the organisation through this committee.

Medical staff composition

A critical question for the hospital's governing board/administration and the medical staff is how to decide which types of practitioners will be granted privileges. The makeup of medical staff directly affects professional support ratios, capital equipment and operating requirements. Yet direct interference by the administration in changing the medical staff composition would be perceived by doctors as a threat to their autonomy.

At Victoria General Hospital, the mix and extension of privileges is decided by the medical staff. But in recognition of institutional difficulties, they have placed upper limits on the number of physicians with privileges within given departments and sub-specialties, in keeping with the hospital's mission and financial resources. New physicians are required to complete an economic impact questionnaire (Table 8.1) and board members granting approval for privileges as recommended by the medical staff are provided with this information. This collaboration has avoided friction and frustration on both sides.

In most major metropolitan centres, there is a surplus of physicans and this puts hospitals in a 'buyer's market'. Technical competance in physicians is no longer enough; increasingly they must give evidence of being cost-effective in their provision of care and 'team players' who will help build the organisation. In Winnipeg, physicians are limited to privileges in two hospitals and it is predicted that in future they are likely to have single hospital appointments, because of the continued surplus.

Building future relationships

The future of the health care industry is very unpredictable, but we will continue to be influenced by population shifts, rising costs, greater consumer expectations and changes resulting from increased specialisation and acuity. The industry will also be affected by a shift in lifestyles, prevention and health promotion. Future relationships between administrative and medical staff will be dependent on strong leadership from the organisation's chief executive officer, clarification of authority and strategies to strengthen the relationships.

The CEO has a pivotal role in building a climate of cooperation for the institution; he or she will listen, mediate, motivate, probe and respond. In addition, it is important to clarify whether decisions will be jointly made by the administration and medical staff or individually by the CEO or medical leaders. Guidelines set up highly visible group structures for promoting more trusting relationships. A cooperative approach to problem solving is suggested in Figure 8.2.

The preparation of physicians for management is a major challenge for them, administrators and the academic community. In 1988, a conference of the Royal College of Physicians and Surgeons of Canada, to prepare a position paper on the responsibility of physicians in hospital planning and management, unsurprisingly concluded that while they have a major role, they are inadequately prepared for it. It is now intended that the educational curriculum for doctors will include the managerial skills training they need. (The Canadian College of Health Service Executives and the Canadian Medical Association have offered Physician Management Institutes across Canada since 1984, and over 600 have attended the three-day seminar. The programme, which is progressive over four levels, has been well received.)

We will be considering part-time managerial appointments for heads of clinical services, in which the individual would give about a quarter of their time to work with the hospital department head who complements their particular service. Some form of compensation would be needed, so it would be important for future medical heads to be selected on relevant criteria rather than popularity. The overall advantage of such a relationship would be the further strengthening of ties below the level of the board and administration.

Finally, provincial governments have been making concerted efforts to reduce the number of hospital beds per thousand population. The ratio has fallen over some 20 years from seven or eight to three or four beds per thousand, and as the population ages and the acuity level of patients has risen significantly, pressures are increasing on an already scarce resource.

Both the hospital and the physicians want to use these beds appropriately. Our medical/administrative advisory committee will review mechanisms to monitor admission and discharge practices, with the assistance of the hospital's computerised system which is linked to the government's computer. The monitoring and review of statistics would serve educational purposes and function on the same basis as the medical audit peer reviews. These rather sensitive areas could not be studied if there were rifts in relationships and a lack of trust.

Figure 8.2

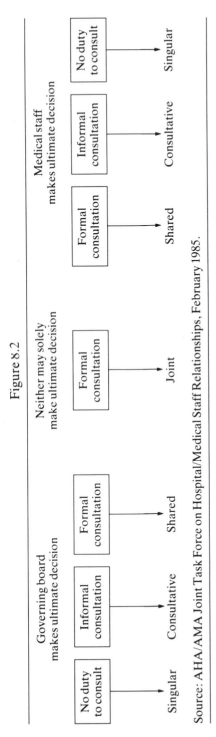

Source: AHA/AMA Joint Task Force on Hospital/Medical Staff Relationships, February 1985.

98

Conclusion

We are often told that problems represent opportunities in disguise. The outcome to future challenges will be growth or erosion, depending on the response of the health care providers. With an optimistic willingness to accept changes in medical models and health care delivery systems, the integrity of the medical profession and hospital services will be maintained.

Reference

Cooperation or conflict: physicians versus administrators. Hospitals, 16 July 1979.

Hospital agreements in Victoria
Connecting summary

	Assessment of health needs	Formulation of objectives and priorities for intervention	Development and operation of programmes	Assessment of impact
Access				
Relevance to needs				
Effectiveness				
Equity				
Social acceptability				
Efficiency and economy				

In any 'agreement' we assume that there is a balance of power between the two parties involved. Another way of putting it, in this context, is that there is a tension between the party responsible for guiding the system and the party responsible for delivering the service. The case study offered by John Morris follows the introduction of health agreements as the focal point of tension between the Department of Health in Victoria and the local hospital services. He addresses eloquently the differing expectations of the central bureaucracy and the local deliverers of service, and the disappointment when neither side's expectations were fulfilled. Neither party would agree that there was a balance of power between them: there was considerable conflict over whether the agreement was intended as a threat and punishment or as a framework for collaboration in the use of limited resources. Morris also mentions the 'felling of trees': one hospital claimed that its first agreement went through 15 drafts and grew to 87 pages. Was it all really necessary?

As with the New Zealand experience, there are many lessons here for all health care systems. I have plotted his study on the efficiency and economy dimension, but have also concluded that there was an attempt to consider each of the four building blocks, including assessment of need and impact of the intervention. What does the reader predict will occur in managing for health result?

HOSPITAL AGREEMENTS IN VICTORIA

John Morris

Any government or central bureaucracy attempting to manage local services or individual institutions has a major problem of ensuring that their managers operate within a common policy and as part of a network providing a chosen pattern of service to particular populations.

At the institutional level, the resources provided have usually been seen as unrelated to the expectations of both government and users of services. The response has been to avoid many management decisions, demanding that these be made at central agency or government levels, and to withdraw into concern solely for the particular institution rather than working as part of a network.

The political and bureaucratic response has often been to resort to direct central management which reduces local capacity to respond to local needs and to tailor services to available resources.

In Victoria, the Minister for Health has supported an attempt to overcome these twin problems through a 'hospital agreements' programme. This involves essentially the negotiation of a formal agreement between the government and each provider agency, specifying a mutually-agreed outcome. This paper describes the background to the introduction of these agreements, the difficulties in starting the programme and some initial views on its efficacy.

Victoria is the smallest of the mainland Australian states, with a land area about equal to that of Great Britain, but with the second highest state population (4.2 million, close to 3 million of whom live in Melbourne and its environs). There are 160 public (government-funded) hospitals: 16 are specialist teaching hospitals; 28 are major metropolitan and country based hospitals; and about 100 are small rural hospitals, all with fewer than 80 beds and some as few as 8. Some 120 private hospitals account for approximately 25 per cent of beds in the state. Victoria has 5.0 beds per 1,000 population, the lowest ratio in the country, whose national average is 5.4 per 1,000. The distribution of beds in Victoria is as low as one per 1,000 in some outer metropolitan areas, and as high as 10 per 1,000 in some rural areas.

Public hospitals in Victoria are incorporated as separate legal entities under the hospital and charities legislation. The governing body is a board of management. Until 1980 this board was elected by 'the contributors' – anyone who donated monies in the previous year. Since then, the board has been appointed by Governor in Council (that is, the Minister of Health). All staff in public hospitals, including the chief executive officers, are employees of the hospital board.

Background to change

The central authority

When the agreement process was begun, the central authority was the Health Commission of Victoria. While in theory independent, it in fact operated as a government department, 'according to the directions of the Minister'. In 1985, the Commission was abolished and the Health Department in Victoria (HDV) created, ostensibly to provide 'greater accountability to the Minister, more streamlined decision-making, and a more responsive and flexible structure'. In practice, the major changes were in personnel and in the title of the department head, from Chairman to Chief General Manager.

Politics

Victoria was governed by a succession of conservative (Liberal/ National Party) governments for 30 years before Labour gained office in 1982. The new Minister for Health, who had held the shadow portfolio for seven years, with a high media profile, began restructuring the Health Commission with the introduction of a regional structure and the appointment of regional directors, half of whom were drawn from the hospital field. He established a review of all capital works and put a hold on all works until its completion. He threatened to remove boards or chief executives who operated at a deficit and announced his intention to redress the distribution of beds across the state through closure, relocation or conversion to nursing homes. He also stopped the custom of adopting the recommendation of boards when filling board vacancies, and required public advertisement of vacant positions.

Industrial relations

The Health Commission had recommended that it take over the industrial role of the Victorian Hospitals Industrial Council, an arm of the state hospital association, VHA. This recommendation arose from the government's concern at a number of costly awards agreed by the Council. A number of health unions were also dissatisfied with dealing with a body which represented hospitals but had no real authority over resources.

The Labour government took central control of all industrial relations in the hospital field. It also established a forum for health unions to relate directly to the Department of Industrial Relations and the Health Committee. It agreed to union demands for a 38-hour week for hospital employees, with a productivity agreement to offset the cost. There was vocal opposition and local dispute over staffing levels when hospitals were instructed to implement the 38-hour week without any financial compensation. At management level, the new industrial procedures led to widespread dissatisfaction, as hospitals perceived (often correctly) that unions could seek redress of fairly minor issues directly with the Department, bypassing local management.

Finances

Until 1983, Victoria's public hospitals were relatively protected from the major cost-cutting exercises of the other states. The smaller number of beds in Victoria meant that the pressure for closure had been less. With a higher proportion of private beds and a high rate of insurance in the community, there was also less pressure on the public system.

No-growth policies had, however, been in force for several years, and many costs – like the 38-hour week – had been absorbed without compensation. Hospitals had steadily reduced whatever financial slack there was.

In 1984, the first real reduction in hospital budgets was imposed. The Minister personally announced a one and a half per cent reduction to a meeting of all chief executive officers and board presidents, acknowledging that hospitals could not sustain the cut without reductions in services. The Health Commission advised the Minister that unless it decided centrally where cuts should be made, hospitals would seek to cut the most politically sensitive services. But the Minister agreed to allow hospitals to decide where the cuts should fall.

Community involvement

An important part of the government's health policy was the promotion of greater community involvement in decisions affecting health services. This was in part the justification for the Minister's insistence on the advertising of board vacancies (although he also believed that the boards were dominated by appointees who would not support the new government's policies). The introduction of regional administration for the Health Commission was also presented as an attempt to increase community involvement. So was the introduction of district health councils – advisory bodies drawn from the community and guaranteed access to department officers, plans and budgets. This last was generally greeted by the hospital system as at best a waste of resources and at worst as a threat to the autonomy of the major institutions.

Conflict

To the Minister and Health Commission, all these changes were aimed at ensuring that the government's policies and priorities for health services were reflected in the operation of the hospitals. In the hospitals' view, the changes in hospital boards were seen as political interference, the introduction of district health councils as usurping their role. The financial cuts seemed to destroy the hospitals' ability to act on their perception of community needs and the centralisation of industrial relations seemed a direct attack on local autonomy. The government's attempts at closure or relocation of hospital beds also generated enormous opposition.

Many hospitals publicly attacked the government over shortage of resources, or applied pressure for more by limiting politically-sensitive services such as open-heart surgery. Waiting lists were made a public issue, initially by some medical staff. Government attempts to defuse growing public concern by injecting resources for specific services were largely negated by a major industrial dispute with the nurses. This meant a rapid rise in waiting lists while the central imposition of a settlement worsened already poor hospital bureaucracy relationships.

Most hospital managements felt that their problems were entirely the result of central actions and some defended their use of political pressure, arguing their responsibility to their patients and the community. The government and central authority believed that hospitals, as government-funded agencies, had little right to use political pressure and so argued for greater restrictions on managements.

By the end of 1984, the media and opposition parties described the situation as a 'hospital crisis' and few in the hospital field disagreed. Hospital services were a major election issue in 1985. When Labour was returned, the Premier replaced the former Minister for Health with the Hon David White, who had a ministerial reputation for firm management and ability to solve major problems.

Mr White announced his intention to establish a Department of

Health, to publish accurate statistics on hospital waiting lists and to demand clear statements of goals and objectives from both the Department and the health agencies. He emphasised his desire to make the Health Commission and the public hospital system much more accountable to both Parliament and the public. Hospitals were attracted by the Minister's assurance that he wanted to work closely with them rather than impose on them, and supported his initiatives. Substantial resources were made available for the strategies to reduce waiting lists.

But new rounds of industrial disputes meant that waiting lists continued to rise. Shortage of nurses caused an even greater reduction in service levels and by late 1985 it was clear that the major problems were not being resolved. Pressure from some hospitals for substantially increased resources was again growing and many were running quite large deficits. Opposition to bed rationalisation was re-emerging.

The inevitable response of the Department and the Minister was greater control over hospital expenditure. Many members of the cabinet called for tougher controls on hospital managements.

It was in this atmosphere that the Minister discussed with the regional directors the relationship between central government and service-providing institutions. It was suggested that the relationship should be that of buyer and seller: the Department should, on behalf of the community, determine what and how much to buy, and at what price, and negotiate to fill these orders with the provider. The Minister accepted this suggestion and two days later announced that he would be establishing hospital contracts specifying the type and price of services to be provided. He described the health department's new role as one of 'strategist, leader and banker' to the health system.

The Minister committed the Department to producing the first Victoria health plan within six months; to contracts designed to ensure that the Department provided leadership and the agencies value for money; for a campaign to increase public understanding of the health system; and to a new organisational structure that gave the health regions considerable responsibility and authority. This was enthusiastically accepted by many hospital managers. Some suggested that a true legal contract could not be achieved within the present legislative framework. So the 'hospital agreements' programme was born.

Managing for health result: hospital agreements

The Minister's stated objective was to gain a mechanism relating the services provided by each agency to the government's overall health plan; to relate resources to an agreed range of service; and thereafter to leave local management free within the framework. He quickly established a departmental committee to develop proposals for hospital agreements and appointed a project manager. In an early report, the committee described the programme as follows:

'*Broad Approach*

Health Service Agreements represent a fundamental change in the management relationship between Government and providers of health services. The program is built around a basic philosophy of delegating greater responsibility to individual health institutions and at the same time increasing their accountability for delivering agreed services and achieving agreed objectives.

The approach is based on annually negotiated agreements between health service providers and the Health Department. These agreements specify objectives, goals and performance indicators and resources and include an acceptance of the need to subsequently report on what is actually achieved in comparison to the agreed objectives and goals.

Perhaps more important and more pervasive is a change in management culture to focus quite specifically on participation and output and performance measurement and reporting in relation to agreed objectives. We are encouraging the adoption of this approach right through to the clinical level and the parallel delegation of day-to-day management responsibility to specific units. Thus, the focus is clearly directed to a style of management that is based on negotiation on what services will be delivered and what processes will be set in place and then providing maximum flexibility and responsibility in day-to-day management with an understanding that each group or body will report on what is achieved as compared to predetermined goals using agreed performance indicators.

Key Aspects

The program is about:

(i) specifying health care and organisational objectives in terms of desired outputs or outcomes;

(ii) determining appropriate indicators that can be used to monitor performance against the agreed objectives and establishing goals and targets for a budget year;

(iii) increasing delegation to operational units for day-to-day management of resources to achieve agreed objectives; and

107

(iv) reporting performance.'

The committee also identified the following key requirements:

An understanding of relevant government policy on:
health care;
industrial relations;
management of public bodies.

An accepted statement of state and regional health plans.

An accepted framework for describing what health service providers offer.

A knowledge of community expectations and attitudes about health policies and services.

An appropriate format for negotation and reporting plans, goals and targets.

Training to develop commitment and skills in objective setting, performance measurement and reporting.

Identification and, where possible, removal of administrative constraints on day-to-day management decision-making.

Pilot programme

The first intention was to pilot one hospital for each of the eight regions, but circumstances restricted this to two metropolitan and two country hospitals. Preparation for the pilot agreements, to run for one year, focused on the development of a standard format; a search for measurable components; training of hospital staff in objective setting performance measurement and reporting; and a survey of community aspirations. A commercial organisation was contracted to do the last and a firm of management consultants to provide training workshops. While the regional directors had some concern to develop regional plans against which proposed agreements could be assessed, the amount of effort put into these plans was by comparison small, with negligible resources.

The Victorian Hospitals Association followed the process with some scepticism, and increasingly represented the interests of the four pilot hospitals, seeking significant incentives for them through the removal of constraints on day-to-day operation and increased budgets and/or flexibility. Conscious of the need to keep the support of the pilot hospitals and the VHA, the Minister instructed the Department to seek real incentives. He was also conscious of his promise that the agreements would be in place at the start of the financial year, which allowed only two months (later extended to four) for the hospitals and Department to undertake an intensive educational programme, develop their goals and statistical framework and negotiate the agreement.

The major issues that concerned the pilot hospitals and the VHA were around autonomy. They had to do with the controls the Department should have over new developments, staffing and recurrent expenditure, and the performance information it would require, as well as the sanctions or rewards which should be built in. The VHA and pilot hospitals argued that the Department should remove all controls other than those specifically covered by the agreement. This was often in conflict with the sections of the Department – like the buildings' division – which had responsibility for overseeing particular activities. Treasury regulations and internal departmental delegations of authority further complicated the matter.

Despite protracted and often tedious negotiations, a form of agreement was prepared. In essence, it described the work of the hospital in terms of patient services, organisation development and management activities, resources, and proposals for capital development, and sought a description of the goals, performance indicators and targets in each of these areas. This part of the agreement was developed in the four hospitals through extensive consultation with staff. The lack of regional plans and detailed information on which to base statistical output measures restricted the targets and performance measures which could be used, and simple measures, such as numbers of patients treated in particular categories, were adopted. People in the pilot hospitals most often felt that this process would have been valuable and helpful even if no agreement had resulted, especially when it involved key members of staff and board members in collective goal and objective setting. It created the opportunity to extend the concept of defined authority and accountability, and so made the decentralisation of decision-making easier.

The major problem in developing the four pilot agreements was over budgets. Two particular aspects caused concern: the inability of the Health Department to finalise grant allocation until some months after the start of the agreement, and the lack of any agreed mechanisms for costing variations from the agreed output. The hospitals argued that the unpredictability of their workload and the effects of industrial situations outside their control made evaluation of performance difficult and complicated. They expressed considerable apprehension about how variations in agreed performance would be treated and tried to set only targets which could be clearly and easily met.

As the total budget for the pilot programme was less than 10 per cent of the overall hospital budget, it proved possible to agree budgets for the pilot hospitals before the Department's allocation was known, as the budget for the rest of the field could be varied adjusted to cover any shortfall. While this helped to meet the objectives of the four hospitals and the timetable laid down by the Minister, it is still not clear how the problem will be resolved when most of the hospitals in Victoria are included in the process.

During the pilot agreement phase, the Health Department also negotiated to establish budget agreements with some 30 other hospitals. It decided to insist that they agreed to a gross budget figure, a revenue budget and associated gross throughput figures, bed days and outpatient attendances, for the financial year. Although not related to the hospital agreements programme, the imposition of these 'agreements' while the broader programme was still being piloted created considerable opposition. Hospitals felt the imposed performance measures and budgets were unrealistic, and there was increased scepticism about the fairness of the Department's negotiating.

Review and expansion

The Minister agreed to hospital demands for greater consultation and established a Hospital Agreements Consultative Committee, comprising Department officers and representatives of the VHA, hospital boards, CEOs and the health unions. To allow the government to extend the agreements programme, the review on which the VHA and hospitals had insisted was brought forward and limited to process, with a promise of a later review of the outcomes of the pilot agreements.

In the first review, made only six months after the pilot agreements had been signed, Mr Len Swindon, previous CEO of the Royal Melbourne Hospital and one of the state's most respected health administrators, argued strongly in support of the principles underlying the programme and for an extension of a modified programme. He stressed the need for the project to be seen as generating attitude change and trust, rather than different control mechanisms. His major criticisms related to the inadequacy of the Department's planning process and the difficulty of framing objectives without regional or state strategic plans; the inadequate time allowed for preparing agreements; the need for widespread education about the programme in the public hospitals; the need for improvements in the budget process; and the need for simplification of the 'model' agreements and appropriate performance and output measures, with delegation to regional directors to negotiate all aspects of the agreements.

The review of outcomes, undertaken in early 1988 by Murray Clarke, another retired senior hospital administrator, concluded that the objective of implementing an output and performance-oriented approach to management had been substantially achieved in the four pilot hospitals. Most hospitals saw agreements as a positive management tool and there was no suggestion of a preferred alternative. The hospital agreements were an opportunity for hospitals to define their future activities, gain autonomy and accept greater accountability.

Clarke thought that simplified contracts, early budget decisions, clarified roles for regional offices and rewards for above-average performance would encourage the field to grasp these opportunities. He also recommended that agreements should be drawn up in two parts: the first covering background, demography, longer-term goals and strategy; the second the actual agreement, with its content limited to service targets, projects and budgets for the year. This would simplify renegotiations.

In 1987/8 the Department, on the basis of Swindon's report and general agreement that the pilot programme had been a success, expanded the programme to cover 30 hospitals, 12 community health centres, five psychiatric centres and three voluntary agencies. The programme was renamed the Health Services Agreement Programme.

There was a substantial revision of the agreement format with a 'strategic focus' through greater emphasis on narrative reports of strategy, environment and the five and ten year hospital plans. Only a third of the document's 90 pages were given to operational goals for the agreement year. Regional officers found it difficult to manage detailed negotiations with a greatly increased number of institutions; all agreements had also to be referred back to the senior management of the Department, which considerably protracted the process.

The VHA meanwhile tried to negotiate an improved set of standard clauses with the Department, but this broke down leaving hospitals to negotiate their own 'non-standard' clauses.

The government imposed an operating budget cut of approaching one per cent and in many cases the Health Department was unable to agree on reasonable patient throughput levels. The Department of Management and Budget also imposed unrealistic revenue targets on the Health Department and, in turn, on the hospitals. Many agreements remained unsigned by November and most hospitals regarded the process of negotiating them in that year as, at least, quite unsatisfactory.

Early benefits

Nevertheless, there have been a number of desirable results from the attempt to develop health agreements. There has been an impetus for the development of state plans. Much effort has been put into developing a description of each hospital and its proposed future and the state and regional plans based on expected needs for services have been related to these descriptions.

Hospitals involved in the process have found that developing their objectives, goals, targets and suitable performance indicators has required real consultation with hospital staff, and that the commitment of staff and the ability of management to control activity within the overall budget have been substantially enhanced.

The pilot agreements were limited to simple specifications of objectives, goals and targets. In several hospitals, the need to develop these descriptions has led to improved internal information, with a general acceptance of the need for more valid measures of both output and outcome.

Two major pilot programmes of full absorption clinical costing have been set up. Several hospitals have used the agreement goals, targets and measures as the basis for regular reports to the board of management and for the hospital annual report.

Early problems

Despite the benefits, very real problems remain.

It is extremely difficult to describe goals in measurable terms, particularly where outcomes of service delivery are desired. The work needed to negotiate a detailed agreement is considerable; one hospital claims its 1987/8 agreement went through 15 drafts and grew to 87 pages.

There has been the problem of finding agreement between a hospital and the Health Department where elements are imposed by a third party and demonstrably unachieveable – for example, the Department of Management and Budget's revenue targets. This has seriously prejudiced the field's acceptance of agreements.

Some hospitals and some department officers have approached the process with unreasonable expectations. Hospitals have believed that they should be able to negotiate increased budgets, while the Department thought it could get agreement to increased outputs with the same or fewer resources. These expectations were disappointed. In some cases, the Department has sought to use details of the agreement to compare hospitals and penalise those seen as less efficient. Although agreement negotiation can provide a more rational basis for the redistribution of the available cake, neither Department nor hospitals seem yet to use it in that way.

Lastly, it has become apparent that many hospital managements have inadequate experience or ability in negotiating. For too long they have been presented with fixed budgets and instructions about performance. For many, achieving a result acceptable to both hospital and Department through discussion has proved most difficult.

The future

Despite quite considerable dissatisfaction with, and scepticism about, the 1987/88 agreements, the government determined that the programme should cover 30 more hospitals and other institutions in 1988/9. Assurances were given of a simpler format, more delegated authority for the negotiating officers and further freedoms from government regulation for hospitals. Murray Clarke's suggestion of a two-part agreement, with only a small part renegotiated each year, was adopted.

Perhaps the best description of the present view is dissatisfaction mixed with guarded optimism. The chief executive officer of the first teaching hospital to sign an agreement and due to negotiate his third, for instance, remained committed to the process. Firstly, he said, it embodied sound management principles, to which few hospitals had an adequate commitment in the past. Secondly, the increased accountability inherent in the system was being steadily revealed. There was the opportunity to establish a rational framework for decision-making and to end the piecemeal and creeping centralisation of authority. And, finally, the relationship between central authority and the hospitals in Victoria had been so bad that any new arrangements were worth trying.

However, it made no sense to speak of agreements when unattainable budgets were imposed by a third party. It was important that the government was aware that health service agreements were aimed at reforming a substantial slice of the public sector. 'Health Service Agreements are the most constructive and potentially far-reaching proposition that has been developed – at least in my 15 years experience of the business – for the planning, funding, organising and controlling the health care system.'

SEEKING EQUITY AND
SOCIAL ACCEPTABILITY

Health care for rural communities in the intermountain region of the United States
Connecting summary

	Assessment of health needs	Formulation of objectives and priorities for intervention	Development and operation of programmes	Assessment of impact
Access				
Relevance to needs				
Effectiveness				
Equity	▓	▓		
Social acceptability				
Efficiency and economy	▓	▓	▓	

'We *can* do anything we want. We take all the risks – financially and to our reputation. What *should* we do?'

Scott Parker's case study of health care in the rural United States illustrated, among other things, the tension within an organisation which is driven by the 'free market' economy and, at the same time, considers itself to have a moral responsibility to its users. This tension was exacerbated by the apparent fact that the organisation holds a monopoly in the delivery of health care to this population: if Intermountain Health Care Incorporated did not provide it, there was no other organisation in the immediate area which could.

Athough Intermountain Health Care has not experienced an acute financial crisis, it does believe in efficiency and effectiveness in order to keep its resources working well for people. There are many parallels with the state-regulated health care systems in the search to provide a service that meets the health needs of all people.

I plotted this tension by locating the case study on the matrix along two dimensions of quality: equity and efficiency and economy. Interestingly, I did not feel able to complete the 'assess impact' box on either dimension. What impact does the reader predict for rural people?'

10

HEALTH CARE FOR RURAL COMMUNITIES IN THE INTERMOUNTAIN REGION OF THE UNITED STATES

Scott S Parker

Intermountain Health Care Incorporated (IHC) is a not-for-profit organisation in the region of the United States which includes the three western states of Utah, Idaho and Wyoming. It makes available a continuum of care ranging from acute inpatient hospital care to out-patient and home care services. The intermountain region has a large number of rural communities, and this case study will concentrate on IHC's development and management of rural health care.

Intermountain Health Care was formed in 1975, when leaders of the Church of Jesus Christ of Latter-day Saints (Mormon) appointed an independent board of trustees and turned over to it all the proper-ties, assets and liabilities of its 15 hospitals. This new board then or-ganised IHC, a not-for-profit corporation without church ties, to own and operate the hospitals.

IHC now operates 24 hospitals with 2,930 beds, including a psychi-atric hospital. In addition, it offers services through 30 rural and urban primary care and specialist clinics, 12 home-health agencies, ten women's centres, and psychiatric and behavioural health units at ten of its hospitals. It has ten blood donor centres, nine urgent care centres, nine pharmacies, seven clinics for the medically needy, three outpatient surgical centres, three dialysis centres, two occupational health centres, inpatient and outpatient rehabilitation programmes, a medical equipment and supply division and a partridge in a pear tree.

IHC has more than 14,000 full-time and part-time employees, with about 2,200 physicians and 2,500 volunteers who each year donate over 400,000 hours of service. It operates its own health insurance scheme, in which over 100,000 people are enrolled.

Intermountain Health Care's activities are guided by its mission and philosophical commitments.

'IHC's mission

Excellence in the provision of health care services to communities in the intermountain region.

IHC's underlying philosophical commitments

Excellent service to our patients, customers and physicians is our most important consideration.

We will provide our services with *integrity*. Our actions will enhance our reputation and reflect the *trust* placed in us by those we serve.

Our employees are our most important resource. We will attract exceptional individuals at all levels of the organization and provide fair compensation and opportunities for personal and professional growth. We will recognize and reward employees who achieve excellence in their work.

We are committed to *serving diverse needs* of the young and old, the rich and poor, and those living in urban and rural communities.

We will reflect the *caring and noble* nature of our mission in all that we do. Our services must be high quality, cost-effective and accessible, achieving a balance between community needs and available resources.

It is our intent to be a *model health care system*. We will strive to be a national leader in not-for-profit health care delivery.

We will maintain the *financial strength* necessary to fulfill our mission.'

IHC is committed to providing care in the sparsely populated, remote areas of rural Utah, southeastern Idaho and southwestern Wyoming, where it is often the sole provider of care. It recognises the special needs of rural people and is dedicated to making available high-quality, cost-effective and accessible services.

Background to change: rural health care in the United States

In the United States, 46 per cent of all hospitals and 23 per cent of hospital beds are in rural communities. The nation's 2,600 rural hospitals, with 217,000 beds, serve 95 million people, or over 40 per cent of the national population. About 350 of these rural hospitals (13 per cent) are their communities' sole providers of care.

Rural hospitals are generally defined as those serving an area with fewer than 2,500 residents or a community which is outside the nation's 261 metropolitan areas. Every region of the country except the District Of Columbia, New Jersey and Rhode Island has a share of these hospitals. In ten states (Alaska, Idaho, Kansas, Mississipi, Montana, Nebraska, North Dakota, South Dakota, Vermont and Wyoming) about 90 per cent of the hospitals are classified as rural. In Utah, 40 per cent of hospitals and 16 per cent of beds are considered rural. Rural hospitals in the remaining states vary between five per cent and 80 per cent of the total.

Trends in rural hospitals

Most rural hospitals are operated as not-for-profit organisations and a quarter are owned, leased or managed by a hospital system. A third of them reported operating deficits of more than six per cent in 1986, and a half of more than 1.5 per cent the following year. In 1986, 68 community hospitals closed in the United States; for the first time since 1981, this included more rural than urban ones (37 and 31). In 1987, half the 80 hospitals which closed were in rural areas, a pattern that was almost identical in 1988. Over 500 more rural hospitals are scheduled to close by 1995.

Because of the financial burdens of providing rural health care, several hospital management companies have also recently decided to discontinue or change their focus. Westworld Community Heathcare for instance, a major for-profit chain which has served rural communities in 14 states, sold 23 ot its 40 rural hospitals in 1987 and then filed for bankruptcy. Hospital Corporation of America, the nation's largest system, has been converting its rural hospitals into outpatient and emergency centres. This trend puts an additional strain on rural communities and on their remaining health care providers.

Most rural hospital losses are related to utilisation and financial challenges. There is excess capacity due to a national shift to outpatient services; an increasing number of people prefer to travel to the city for health care because they think the quality higher there; average occupancy rates are only 55 per cent in rural hospitals compared to 68 per cent in urban ones. On the financial side, there is a growing number of unpaid bills, decreasing reimbursement from Medicare, increasing costs and constrained resources and depression in rural economies which means less community support for the hospital.

Analysts note that trends in rural health may be due not so much to the rural environment as to nationwide changes in the health care industry and the economy. But most agree that unfavourable patterns are intensified in rural areas. Rural hospitals also feel increasing pressure to provide free care for poor people and to offer a range of services that may be more efficiently provided at larger facilities.

The increasing hardships of rural hospitals have attracted much attention from the United States Congress and various rural health coalitions representing the hospitals. Smaller ones are beginning to consolidate their operations and to find ways to join with other rural hospitals or larger urban ones in order to survive.

Barriers to rural health care

Several barriers are common across the United States:

Environment: isolated communities often have geographical barriers which affect timely transport to, and communications with, health resources.

Income: a higher percentage of rural than urban residents live below the federal poverty level; fewer resources are available for health care.

Unemployment: high unemployment rates and a high percentage of jobs in agriculture and small businesses that are seasonal or do not offer private health insurance mean that rural workers have inadequate cover.

Age: rural communities have a growing proportion of the country's elderly population, who often have multiple, chronic health problems but limited finances and access to care; retirement communities for elderly people are typically located in rural areas.

Health education: rural residents often lack up-to-date information on preventive health, because few health educators wish to work in rural areas.

Hospital resources: rural hospitals find it hard to attract and retain physicians, especially specialists, and other professionals. The hospitals also lack the funds to purchase and upgrade equipment and facilities.

Because of these and other barriers, rural health needs often go unmet. The concentration of older people who need costly care and poor people who cannot pay their bills exacerbates the problem of insufficient resources.

IHC's rural health care

About 58 per cent of IHC's hospitals and a quarter of its beds are in rural areas in Utah, Idaho and Wyoming. It operates 14 rural hospitals, with 689 beds and 25 hospital-sponsored rural primary care clinics, for a combined population of 385,000 people. Eight of these hospitals are their county's sole provider and 11 have fewer than 70 beds. Although rural hospitals provide valuable patient referrals to other IHC facilities, a significant number of rural patients are lost to non-IHC hospitals.

Most of IHC's rural hospitals are typical of such places nationwide. Profit margins have been steadily declining and occupancy rates have

Table 10.1   Utilisation and financial history: total IHC small rural hospitals

	Total beds	Total patient days	Average occupancy rate %	Gross revenue $	Average profit margin %
1983	354	42,661	49.7	26,044,121	1.9
1984	363	38,795	47.7	27,488,975	(2.8)
1985	345	33,975	45.3	28,093,724	(4.4)
1986	325	32,600	38.7	36,434,710	(5.1)
1987	325	32,231	25.0	38,893,780	(6.0)
1988	325	31,200	23.2	45,226,801	(7.6)

been falling faster than in IHC's non-rural hospitals. Rural hospital losses are increasing, with an aggregate loss of $3.4m in 1988 and a projected loss of a further million or more (aggregate). (See Tables 10.1 and 10.2 and, for comparison with IHC's non-rural hospitals, Table 10.3.) IHC's response to this is to convert empty acute beds in hospitals with fewer than 50 beds for long-term care needs. This allows the hospitals to use their existing resources while meeting a variety of community needs.

IHC has also developed alternatives to hospital care in its rural communities; where appropriate, patients receive follow-up treatment at home rather than in costly hospital settings. Since 1983, IHC has participated in a rural health long-term care programme, originally grant-funded, in which service coordinators in seven IHC hospitals in Utah assess the needs of about 200 patients in their communities, arrange for services – whether skilled nursing or housework – and monitor their care. This programme, designed to enable many of Utah's rural elderly people to remain at home, has been effective in delaying or eliminating their need for costly nursing home care.

IHC extends its continuing medical education programmes to rural physicians and other health workers through a satellite system at all its hospitals. At five rural hospitals in Utah, more than a dozen IHC physicians are salaried employees, with the objective of retaining them in the rural communities and providing them with a secure income, as well as covering their malpractice insurance. Paying physicians' salaries is a recent departure for IHC's rural hospitals and physicians have responded well in one pilot setting.

In 1987, IHC worked closely with the Utah State Health Department and the Utah Hospital Association on a study of the plight of small rural hospitals. The taskforce recommended to the legislature

Table 10.2   Combined income statements: total IHC small rural hospitals

	1983 $	1984 $	1985 $	1986 $	1987 $	1988 $
Daily hospital service	7,569,507	7,494,163	7,101,367	8,007,163	7,893,690	8,700,421
Inpatient ancillary	11,364,673	11,896,211	11,538,582	14,941,659	15,542,885	17,889,944
Outpatient ancillary	5,964,867	7,079,711	8,362,893	12,219,526	13,974,024	17,069,599
Long-term care	1,145,074	1,018,890	1,090,882	1,266,362	1,483,181	1,566,837
Gross revenue	26,044,121	27,488,975	28,093,724	36,434,710	38,893,780	45,226,801
Deductions	3,417,044	3,721,804	2,997,682	4,857,300	5,016,608	7,963,315
Net patient revenue	22,627,077	23,767,171	25,096,042	31,577,410	33,877,172	37,263,486
Other operating revenue	361,202	502,649	805,397	1,304,859	1,316,785	1,478,144
Total operating revenue	22,988,279	24,269,820	25,901,439	32,882,269	35,193,957	38,741,630
Salaries and wages	10,496,092	10,881,766	11,339,437	14,227,902	15,832,993	17,874,616
Employee benefits	2,042,216	2,470,927	2,652,166	3,124,276	3,521,336	3,890,266
Medical professional fees	1,661,737	2,063,651	1,990,915	3,038,897	3,250,427	3,622,397
Non-medical professional fees	530,257	430,007	451,985	290,532	331,487	256,067
Medical surgical supplies	2,365,997	2,520,376	2,605,636	3,016,089	3,156,438	3,544,005
Non-medical/surgical supplies	1,135,546	1,233,292	1,237,285	1,413,136	1,497,970	1,052,721
Purchased utilities	816,464	907,481	986,082	1,164,755	1,196,192	1,236,337
Other purchased services	1,272,714	1,279,131	1,367,340	1,560,405	1,552,376	1,700,526
Other expenses	506,167	668,343	777,301	871,516	944,989	1,176,414
Transfers	97,282	273,079	624,689	1,162,935	1,341,398	2,509,721
Subtotal expenses	20,924,472	22,728,053	24,032,836	29,870,443	32,625,606	36,863,070
Contribution	2,063,807	1,541,767	1,868,603	3,011,826	1,251,566	400,416
Interest expense	42,693	333,737	497,653	1,511,750	1,577,650	1,610,708
Depreciation and amortization	716,762	1,014,953	1,472,358	2,033,806	2,112,671	2,369,807
Corporate charge	815,052	976,118	1,125,584	1,330,620	1,224,839	1,338,412
Subtotal	1,574,507	2,324,808	3,095,595	4,876,176	4,915,160	5,318,927
Total expenses	22,498,979	25,052,861	27,128,431	34,746,619	37,540,766	42,181,997
Net income	489,300	(783,041)	(1,226,992)	(1,864,350)	(2,346,809)	(3,440,367)
Earnings before interest and taxes	531,993	449,304	(729,339)	352,600	769,158	(1,829,659)
Average profit margin	1.9%	(2.8%)	(4.4%)	(5.1%)	(6.0%)	(7.6%)

123

Table 10.3   Combined income statements: total IHC non-rural hospitals

	1983 $	1984 $	1985 $	1986 $	1987 $	1988 $
Daily hospital service	121,012,558	127,126,001	137,095,201	149,839,176	167,879,110	180,255,207
Inpatient ancillary	158,081,486	168,523,810	190,246,890	209,077,452	246,715,621	285,772,882
Outpatient ancillary	47,327,052	60,332,013	75,816,271	87,822,281	109,161,014	142,778,404
Other revenue	4,635,660	7,785,472	6,324,363	6,771,153	5,974,507	22,194,456
Gross revenue	331,056,756	363,767,296	409,482,725	453,510,062	529,730,252	631,100,953
Deductions	39,618,269	25,171,585	31,738,441	41,679,547	68,584,322	97,527,831
Net patient revenue	291,438,487	338,595,711	377,744,284	411,830,514	461,145,930	533,573,122
Other operating revenue	11,429,818	14,126,103	16,535,504	22,135,663	23,904,837	28,961,799
Total operating revenue	302,868,305	352,721,813	394,279,788	433,966,178	485,050,767	562,534,921
Salaries and wages	139,393,360	151,516,399	172,237,633	195,427,302	218,651,740	262,346,222
Employee benefits	22,157,505	28,962,034	29,637,653	33,150,384	39,016,390	31,627,370
Medical professional fees	14,317,898	15,674,845	17,158,641	17,515,825	20,910,989	23,668,575
Non-medical professional fees	1,698,907	2,560,894	4,302,770	4,966,824	4,781,564	6,260,699
Medical/surgical supplies	40,817,265	45,060,281	50,628,647	54,822,562	60,843,651	69,441,765
Non-medical/surgical supplies	13,864,629	14,699,256	17,872,642	19,502,799	21,332,641	26,539,075
Purchased utilities	6,858,838	8,573,568	9,437,095	10,132,535	10,951,526	12,160,424
Other purchased services	15,139,345	18,550,098	21,377,293	24,496,851	26,744,486	31,412,504
Other expenses	8,136,469	10,602,445	15,603,921	21,019,253	18,743,342	41,708,638
Transfers	4,610,978	3,412,891	7,949,106	9,528,387	(8,981,486)	(15,570,501)
Subtotal expenses	266,995,194	299,612,711	346,205,401	390,562,722	412,994,843	489,594,771
Contribution	35,873,111	53,109,102	48,074,387	43,403,456	72,055,924	72,940,150
Interest expense	7,557,061	11,575,146	14,388,185	15,375,741	16,125,430	17,178,494
Depreciation and amortization	15,679,871	21,465,173	26,435,669	28,932,757	31,848,389	36,752,714
Total expenses	280,000,555	324,304,972	371,860,156	415,692,743	460,968,662	543,525,979
Net income	22,867,750	28,416,842	22,419,632	18,273,734	24,082,105	28,008,942
Average profit margin	6.9%	7.8%	5.5%	4.0%	4.5%	4.4%

that these hospitals establish closer ties with local physicians and larger referral hospitals and that state and local health departments continue to support programmes, projects and physician recruitment efforts that foster the continued provision of accessible health care in Utah's rural communities.

Recently, several non-IHC rural hospitals in Utah have approached the organisation for its help. These hospitals are struggling because of occupancy and financial challenges, and seeking financial resources. Because of IHC's strength as a hospital system and its commitment to rural communities, it may be better placed than most others to provide rural health care. Although it is not currently in the market for additional hospitals, it has been able to offer expertise and consultant assistance to help those hospitals meet their own communities' needs.

Future directions in rural health care: some questions

As a large, integrated health care system, IHC has multiple and sometimes competing priorities. But it remains committed to making rural health care a priority for the system and is currently developing a corporation-wide strategy for it. It realises that changes in the organisation, management and staffing of rural services may be necessary in future. While in the past, for instance, it has been concerned about the financial viability of only one or two of its rural hospitals, now six are in jeopardy. Nevertheless, IHC is currently exploring options for increasing the viability of its small rural hospitals so that they can continue to provide needed care.

The rural hospitals are effective entry points for patients into the IHC system. They also provide valuable referrals to IHC's non-rural hospitals. In 1987 alone, they referred over 4,600 patients, a financial contribution of nearly $10m. So it may be in the non-rural hospitals' best interests to continue to subsidise, at least partially, the system's rural facilities. However, the declining profit margins of the non-rural hospitals in recent years (see Table 10.3) suggests that it will be increasingly difficult for them to continue the subsidy at the present level of some $3.44m a year. Although this represents only 0.5 per cent of the non-rural hospitals' gross patient revenues, it is over 12 per cent of their total net income.

One of IHC's dilemmas is uncertainty about how to measure accurately the value of the referrals from rural hospitals. If those hospitals did not exist, IHC's larger hospitals might be able to capture the patients anyway, through direct outreach. So the subsidy is not necessarily profitably counterbalanced by the amount of referrals. Nevertheless, IHC does recognise the value of this contribution and has changed its philosophy over the years to try to evaluate rural hospitals more fairly.

Questions for discussion

Given IHC's mission, are rural hospitals necessarily part of its commitment to its communities?

What are IHC's obligations in terms of rural health care?

Who should be responsible for providing health care to rural communities?

Health Care for a medically indigent population in St Louis
Connecting summary

	Assessment of health needs	Formulation of objectives and priorities for intervention	Development and operation of programmes	Assessment of impact
Access				
Relevance to needs				
Effectiveness				
Equity		░		
Social acceptability		░	░	
Efficiency and economy		░	░	

The 'human face of capitalism' lives – but only just. This is a case study of an organisation struggling to serve people who are not insured by the American system of health care – people who do not thrive in the American economy. The organisation was established in a very unstable environment, with no working capital, inadequate financial plans and an inadequate budget. Its ability to generate income is extremely limited in a situation which continually demands more: more money, more technology and more professionally-trained people.

Robert Johnson's case study highlighted the difficulty of managing for health result when the forces for change include racial polarisation and political imperative to reorganise local publicity-funded health care. It is hard to know whether the organisational chaos is one of the forces for change or one of its consequences. But a high degree of commitment and energy is going into delivering a service to poor people in St Louis.

I chose to plot this case study on three dimensions of quality and two of the building blocks. There was a clear mandate to redress the inequality of care to a specific population, facilitated by the political agendas of social acceptability and integrated health care system. Nothing could be achieved that was not socially acceptable to the electorate. In addition, the service's survival depended on more efficient and cost-effective management: its right to exist was not given. Management processes fell for the most part into the setting of objectives and priorities and of certain operational plans, to meet the expectations of any conflicting groups. I did not think the management had yet reached the stage of assessing the impact of their programmes. Would the service's survival be one of the health results? What does the reader think?

11

HEALTH CARE FOR A MEDICALLY INDIGENT POPULATION IN ST LOUIS

Robert Johnson

The St Louis Regional Health Care Corporation was established in 1985 with no working capital, inadequate financial plans and inadequate budget. About a third of its growing number of patients are medically indigent; nearly all the rest rely on Medicare or Medicaid.

This paper chronicles the development of the organisation, from its highly political beginnings, through continued political complications, to the development of more professional organisation and delivery of health care.

The St Louis Regional Health Care Corporation was established in July 1985 with the express purpose of replacing City Hospital and County Hospital, which both closed that year. This was the culmination of four years of effort by the Mayor of the City of St Louis to realise his campaign promise to improve the publicly-funded health care system, and to establish a coherent pattern to which the city government could relate.

St Louis Regional Health Care Corporation is a private not-for-profit organisation, with four main components:

St Louis Regional Medical Center is a 300-bed general hospital, with specialty clinics and a home-care programme.

Four community-based ambulatory (walk in) care centres are managed by the Corporation and owned by the City of St Louis.

St Louis Regional Professional Services Corporation is a not-for profit organisation set up to provide physician services through contracts with institutions and independent professionals.

An Educational and Research Foundation is geared to acquiring research and educational grants.

St Louis Regional Health Care Corporation is governed by a 15-member board of directors, seven nominated by the Mayor of St Louis, seven by the County Executive, St Louis County, and the chairman jointly nominated by both. The Corporation has contracts with both city and county for the provision of care to the medically indigent of their jurisdictions. Approximately 90 days before the beginning of their fiscal year (both of which are different from the Corporation's) it submits an estimate of the cost of care; city and county pay their proportion, less anticipated cash receipts. Both jurisdictions share equally in debt repayments for the purchase and renovation of the hospital and also in the cost of care of patients from outside their jurisdictions. At the end of the hospital's fiscal year, there is a settlement with city and county; our contract lays down that we can neither keep a surplus nor continue a deficit.

In 1988–9 we expected to admit slightly under 11,600 patients, to provide approximately 42,000 specialty clinic visits and 174,000 outpatient visits through the four community care centres, and to provide more than 16,000 home care visits. About 30 per cent of our patients are uninsured and so medically indigent; about 24 per cent have Medicare, 38 per cent Medicaid and 8 per cent commercial insurance or other cover.

Background to change

St Louis is an urban centre with a population of 453,000; St Louis County, the suburban community immediately adjacent, has a population of 973,000 (1980 census). The city has experienced a major loss of population from a high of 857,000 inhabitants in 1950. Its population now is 54 per cent white, 46 per cent black and less than 1 per cent Hispanic and others. St Louis County is approximately 88 per cent white and 11 per cent black. In 1980, per capita family income in the city was $11,782, compared with $29,213 in the county; almost 17 per cent of city residents, compared with 3.5 per cent of county ones, live below the federal poverty line, and 14 per cent of city residents, compared with 3.5 per cent of county ones, receive public assistance. Over 100,000 residents of the city are uninsured and medically indigent, with incomes at or below 150 per cent of the federal poverty level. (Approximately 37 million Americans are considered medically indigent; almost one million Missourians, nearly 20 per cent of its population, are uninsured or underinsured.)

There are also significant differences in the political and governmental structures of city and county. The city has a 'weak mayoral system', in that the Mayor shares budgetary authority with the President of the Board of Aldermen (the elected local legislative body) and the Comptroller, elected chief fiscal officer. In St Louis County, the structure is made up of the elected County Executive and a seven-member (legislative) county council. However, the Mayor, Vincent C Schoemehl, has proved a very strong chief executive since his election in 1981. He is a Democrat, as are most of the elected city officials. The County Executive, elected in 1974, is a Republican, as are four members of the county council. But in spite of the differences, the two chief executive officers formed a personal friendship which contributed to their willingness to plan and support the closure of their public hospitals and replace these with the St Louis Regional Health Care Corporation.

The City of St Louis has had a long history of racial polarisation principally reflected in the fact that most black residents live in North St Louis and most white residents in the South. Before 1954, the city had two public hospitals, legally mandated for the care of black and white patients respectively.

Homer G Phillips, the hospital serving the black community, was established in 1934 and has trained more than 40 per cent of black surgeons in the United States. In 1979, this hospital was closed by the then Mayor, in a manner that provoked loud and sustained protest, even though it was newer than City Hospital, the other public hospital. Police, helicopters and police dogs were used to cordon off the hospital and close it. Various organisations have continued to campaign for its re-opening.

The current Mayor was elected in part on his promise to do this, with support from 97 per cent of the black community. Between 1981 and 1985, he pursued a number of initiatives to reorganise the city's publicly-funded health care system. In 1982, a bond issue was placed on the ballot to raise $64m to re-open Homer G Phillips Hospital, together with an initiative to permit the city to contract with an outside firm to run it. Both initiatives failed to get the necessary majority.

Between 1981 and 1985, the Mayor pursued a number of other initiatives to reorganise the city's publicly-funded health care, including a taskforce of health professionals and civic and community leaders which was co-chaired by the two men who were eventually to co-chair the board of the new St Louis Regional Health Care Corporation.

In 1982, City Hospital lost its accreditation from the Joint Commission on the Accreditation of Hospitals; the following year, the Mayor announced plans to close it which were later withdrawn. Accreditation was restored, but St Louis University signalled its intention to discontinue its affiliation with the hospital by mid-1985. In 1984, the city contracted with National Medical Enterprise (NME), a large proprietary hospital company, to manage City Hospital, which it did until the hospital closed in 1985.

Also in 1984, St Luke's Hospital, which owned the building that is now the St Louis Regional Medical Center, was sold to Charter Medical Corporation, a for-profit chain based in Georgia. But it became apparent that Charter could not make a financial go of the facility, and the Mayor threatened to take it by eminent domain if Charter did not sell it to the city.

In June 1985, the Mayor, with the support of the County Executive, decided to close City Hospital and support the establishment of St Louis Regional Health Care Corporation, with the express purpose of buying the Charter Hospital. The subsequent closure of County Hospital by November that year was part of the plan. City Hospital was closed in June and patients were transferred to the Charter, now St Louis Regional Medical Center. The new Corporation was officially established in July.

Establishing the St Louis Regional Health Care Corporation

Murphy's law has not been repealed: 'if anything can go wrong, it will'. That adequately describes the start of the Corporation.

We started the operation, which spent some $54m during the first year, with no working capital, inadequate financial plans, and an inadequate budget from the City of St Louis. There were significant delays in setting up the system that permits billing to Medicare and Medicaid; there was inefficient physician billing by National Medical Enterprises, which had been running City Hospital and was contracted to run the new one. All this resulted in a major cash flow short-fall in the first year of operation.

We also experienced significant organisational and operational problems. Our first employees were formerly employed by City, County and Charter hospitals. In many cases, we were paying people (with essentially equal qualifications and doing approximately the same job) different rates based on their former pay scales. There was a great deal of chaos in merging the large volume of medical records from City Hospital and City clinics into a new records system which also had to maintain records from Charter and St Luke's Hospitals.

We found it difficult to recruit and retain enough registered nurses – which partly reflected local and national difficulties but was compounded by the fact that our salary structure was not locally competitive.

Our physical plant was superior to that of either City or County Hospitals; we had private or semi-private air-conditioned rooms and fairly attractive buildings which had been reasonably well maintained. But the size of the emergency room was inadequate for our patient volume and there was no obstetrical and newborn service at all when we started.

Like any new organisation, it took us a while to develop clear-cut policies and procedures for the operation of the hospital and clinics. The National Medical Enterprise's contract to manage the hospital was phased out between February 1986, when I became President and Chief Executive Officer, and September of that year. But two

NME employees, the director of nursing and the associate director of ancillary and support services, were retained, partly to create some stability. This, however, suggested the continued presence of NME, which contributed to a lack of trust within the organisation. In addition, racial strife, in part reflected by the lack of minorities in senior management, was compounded by the salary disparities between the former employees of City, County and Charter Hospitals.

As well as dealing with all these operational, organisational and financial problems, we found ourselves at the centre of a great deal of political turmoil. The single most visible factor was a breach between the Mayor and Congressman William Clay Sr, a former ally. Congressman Clay is believed to have opposed the creation of the St Louis Regional Health Care Corporation because this meant the closure of City Hospital; most employees there were union members, and Congressman Clay has had a long history of strong union support. He tried to nullify the contract between ourselves and the City of St Louis, but without success.

There has also been a continuing community opposition, principally from former employees of the Homer G Phillips Hospital and political health advocates concerned about political accountability and access to services by the medically indigent. Many of the community critics joined an organisation called Health Care is a Human Rights Coalition. Although our opponents are relatively few, we have received a great deal of media attention.

Organisational development

During its first three and a half years, St Louis Regional Health Care Corporation has become more stable, and has begun to improve its organisation, operational planning, long-range strategic planning, patient relations and financial management.

The corporation has been reorganised and a number of top administrative posts have been filled. We now have an executive vice-president for operations (chief operating officer); the administrator for ambulatory care now reports directly to the chief executive officer and is responsible for only the community clinics; responsibility for supervision of home care and establishing the physician billing system has been transferred to the medical director (now vice-president for medical affairs).

The hospital has a three-year accreditation from the Joint Commission on the Accreditation of Hospitals and had its four community clinics accredited and certified as hospital-based clinics – the first time in their existence that they have been licensed by the state of Missouri. In 1987, we established a self-insurance trust fund for medical malpractice with general liability coverage, thus stabilising the cost of medical malpractice and general liability coverage at some $4m a year.

At the operational planning level, we established a set of departmental goals and objectives for fiscal years 1987 and 1988. We developed a process of identifying and correcting operational problems, and completed the necessary relocation of all sub-specialty clinics. We developed an 18 month to two year plan to improve the ambulatory care service, renovated a haemodialysis unit, expanded the size of the emergency room and established a nearby satellite x-ray unit. We have a new 32-bed obstetrics and 18-bed gynaecology unit, with a 26-bed neonatal special care and intermediate care unit. We increased the number of nurses by more than 100. We have an active quality assurance programme in the hospital and the clinics, and a recently-established risk management programme. We have a patient representative programme, a multidisciplinary patient advocacy committee of the staff, a guest relations programme and a patients relations committee of the board of directors. We introduced a year-long training programme in interpersonal skills and communications for all employees. We have a 24-hour patients' complaints hot line.

In spite of our serious financial problems, we have improved our collections from $15m in the first year to $34m in the third. During our first three fiscal years, our expenses rose by 30.5 per cent, or an average of 10.2 per cent. During the same time, admissions increased by 69.6 per cent, primary clinic visits by 62.5 per cent, and patient days by 52.5 per cent. The percentage of our budget that came from City and County declined from 67 per cent to 49.7 per cent. Our new computer system has significantly improved the recording of revenue and expenses, improved billing and collections, and improved the efficiency of registration and admission of patients. Once the system is fully implemented, we will be able to transmit the ordering of ancillary studies and their results between our various care sites.

Problems and concerns

Any assessment of this approach to providing health care to the medically indigent population needs to recognise that we must be continually alert to certain problems and concerns.

There will continue to be very significant economic pressure on health care delivery in general and on organisations that serve the medically indigent in particular.

There is great potential for conflict between members of the board of directors, because many of them are employees of city or county.

Strategic issues

The St Louis Regional Health Care Corporation faces five major strategic issues over the next five or more years.

Acquiring and maintaining sufficient resources to provide predictable high quality care. This will be extremely difficult in the face of an erosion in funding for Medicare, the size of our medically indigent population, the reduced capacity of private hospitals to provide charity care and the inadequate tax base of local government.

Funding ways to provide cost-effective services while maintaining acceptable quality. This depends partly on finding predictable financial resources, to allow for planning and implementation of strategic change. It also means establishing a measurable base for determining the cost-effectiveness of care and services.

Acquiring and maintaining community support. This is especially important for health care organisations that rely on public funds. It depends on local understanding of the role and mission of the organisation and the extent to which this is being met, on patients' perception that they receive dignified and respectful care, and on the extent to which the organisation is seen as publicly accountable.

Developing an equitable and predictable funding base for tertiary care services. We currently provide only limited tertiary care services, such as neonatal intensive care and haemodialysis. We do not yet provide high cost technological diagnostic services nor such sophisticated clinical services as burn care, psychiatric services, drug and alcohol treatment and organ transplantation, and explicit financial arrangements must be made to ensure their availability.

Coordinating and integrating primary ambulatory care services. There are five federally-funded health centres in the community and we need to ensure that there is no duplication of services between these and our own centres, and that there is a continuum of care for the medically indigent members of the community, irrespective of where they receive primary care.

Conclusions

There are many real challenges ahead. St Louis Regional Health Care Corporation will have a major role in such difficult public health and public policy issues as care of AIDS patients, improving the care of women and children, so reducing infant mortality, improving care of the elderly and continuing to reduce the high cost of care while solving the problem of medical indigency.

At this point, it can be said that we have improved the use of city and county resources for the health care of the medically indigent. Our physical plant is better and more economical than the facilities it replaced. We have developed an integrated health care system that combines primary, secondary and some tertiary services, with a framework for physician-hospital cooperation. We have also made the organisation and delivery of care somewhat less political and more professional.

Building new partnerships with the Maori people
Connecting Summary

	Assessment of health needs	Formulation of objectives and priorities for intervention	Development and operation of programmes	Assessment of impact
Access				
Relevance to needs				
Effectiveness				
Equity	▓	▓		
Social acceptability	▓	▓		
Efficiency and economy				

Where does a government intervene to 'do the right thing' in a society where there have been so many 'wrongs', both real and perceived? This case study considers how to make fundamental changes in the New Zealand health care system in a way that facilitates the inclusion of Maori people. The Maori people have been considerably disempowered; their history is filled with broken promises and miscommunication and, as George Salmond has already pointed out, New Zealand's health care system is not serving changing needs of the people at large. There are new opportunities to grow strong in traditional and contemporary ways and for both Maori and *pakeha* cultures to gain. Management is about decentralisation and partnership.

I have plotted Glenn Garlick's case study in the two quality dimensions, equity and social acceptability. As in Robert Johnson's study, there is a real attempt to redress inequality, here considerably helped by a perspective of equity that is national rather than local. In addition, the social acceptability of the service to the Maori people is critical. In the presentation of this case study the building blocks were the assessment of health needs and the formulation of objectives and priorities for intervention. I did not feel that there had yet been development of operational plans or assessment of the impact of decisions. What predictions does the reader make about the services' ability to help the Maori people express their uniqueness while also being integrated into the health system?

BUILDING NEW PARTNERSHIPS WITH THE MAORI PEOPLE

Glenn Garlick

In New Zealand, health and other social services are increasingly moving towards decentralisation and political partnership with the Maori people. In April 1988, the government announced plans to abolish the Department of Maori Affairs and devolve management of services for Maori people to tribal (*iwi*) authorities. This paper examines the background to such movements and some of the possible developments in health services. It questions whether any health services can ever be a stable state, or whether health managers are working in an ever-changing environment the focus of which continually alters to concentrate on factors that, for the moment, contribute to better health.

Background to change

The treaty of Waitangi, signed in 1840, has been described as establishing a partnership between the indigenous Maori inhabitants of Aotearoa and the British Crown and, in an international sense, as marking the beginning of nationhood. The treaty was prepared in haste by a number of contributors; different people worked on the English and Maori versions (Appendix 1). Arguments about the treaty as expression of intent, legally binding contract or something in between have been a constant feature of Maori political life ever since. In the 1980s, recognition of the treaty, or of its principles, has also been a major factor in the New Zealand political scene.

The second article of the English translation of the Maori version of the treaty refers to the Crown's protection of the people of New Zealand in the unqualified exercise of their chieftainship over 'all their treasures' ('*taonga*'). The application of the term *taonga* is a matter of great debate. The Official Language Act of 1988, for instance, makes the Maori language one of New Zealand's two official languages; a major argument within the act was that *te reo* (the language) was a specific treasure protected by the treaty. There has not yet been as strong an identification of health, well-being or balance as *taonga* to be cherished under legislation.

The legal status of the treaty has been debated over many years. The Waitangi Tribunal has considered submissions related to many grievances and claims of injustice by Maori tribal authorities. The extent of these claims and the fact that the tribunal is empowered to consider grievances dating back to 1840 has created considerable social tension. Two decisions of the court have been of great moment. In a landmark decision, the Court of Appeal has barred the transfer of assets, mainly land, from the Crown to state-owned enterprises where those assets were subject to claims before the Waitangi Tribunal. A clause in the Fisheries Act precludes any action contrary to the treaty, so when fisheries licences came up for review, the selling of these was immediately suspended (see Article the second of the treaty). These findings and others have resulted in an understandable reluctance to refer to the treaty in legislation. The State Sector Act of 1988, for instance, which established general managers in the health service, made no general reference to the treaty.

A major issue for health service managers will be to consider the relationship between political and social contracts likely to be included within legislation. The identification of social justice as a health result, or a prerequisite to achieving other health results, will become a major national and local issue.

Maori and health

About 13 per cent of the total population is Maori by self-definition (1986 census). The generally disadvantaged social and economic position of Maori is associated with poor infant health and high levels of alcohol abuse, smoking and hospital admission rates.

A prerequisite to the establishment of practical political and economic power in the hands of Maori is the definition of Maori. Research in the Waikato Hospital has tried to establish patient-determined ethnicity and canoe/tribe/subtribe affiliation at the time of hospital admission (Maori ancestry is traced back to one of a number of canoes which brought ancestors to the country). This survey showed that only about 20 per cent of people identifying themselves as of Maori descent displayed accurate knowledge of their canoe/tribe/subtribe. This finding is highly significant in relation to current government policy to devolve authority and resources directly to *iwi* (tribes). For such a policy to be generally effective, there will need to be a significant investment in re-establishing traditional canoe/tribe/subtribe links. Alternatively, many Maori may choose to 'enrol' with their district-based health service unit rather than to follow the *iwi*-based unit.

The Maori view of health is a holistic one. It comprises the dimensions of:

taha wairua – spiritual dimension
taha tinana – physical dimension
taha hinengaro – mental dimension
taha whanau – family dimension

The injustices of the past, particularly in relation to land and the loss of *mana* (prestige, pride) resulting from that, have disturbed the essential balance within and between those dimensions. They are seen as directly related to the low socio-economic position and low self-esteem which is at the base of poor health status. Improvements in health status are clearly unlikely to spring from health services alone. Health is understandably at the top of a health services manager's priority list. But is it at the top of the Maori agenda?

Maori social relationships have had a clear structural framework based on the *whanau/hapu/iwi* – the family/subtribe/tribe. There is growing recognition of the tribe as the system through which social policy should be established and implemented, and services provided. But local government boundaries take no cognisance of tribal ones. (The major local government reform of 1988 and 1989, replacing the plethora of authorities with a new structure of regions and districts, ensures that area health board district boundaries will in almost all cases coincide with local government regional ones. But there have been difficulties with Maori partnership and amendments to the empowering legislation are being considered which recognise Maori input in the new structures.) In addition, the sectoral divisions of government housing, welfare, health and education services and the relative emphasis on individuals does not link easily to the holistic view of health or the more collective pattern of Maori social relationships. Further, government-sponsored Maori organisations – district Maori councils, trust boards – have different district structures.

While it is unreliable to define the Maori view of health in other than Maori terms, there are strong similarities between it and the primary health care philosophy. Health has been a major part of the government's review of social services. But unfortunately the major structural innovation in the health service, the formation of area health boards, is unspecific in relation to primary health care. Nevertheless, the formation of area health boards has wide Maori support because of the increased emphasis on health promotion and care outside institutions. The transition also provides an opportunity for power-sharing through new structures.

Urbanisation and migration have greatly disturbed tribal identification with geographical areas. Thus people living in a city may have a tribal affiliation hundreds of kilometres away. In such cir-cumstances, other Maori organisations, which may be non-tribal or multi-tribal, become important. These may be based at urban *marae* (meeting places) or be national organisations, such as the Maori Women's Welfare League. Tribal identification is important if the tribe is to become a viable organisation concerned with, among other things, the health of the tribe and its members.

Purpose and intended values: external

New and relevant values are being initiated from many sources. These include the national political environment, local communities, local governing bodies such as the Waikato Hospital Board, the Maori people, tribal authorities and individuals. At the moment, the strongest value shifts are externally imposed, mainly from national level. These are most clearly seen in policies of devolution and bicul-turalism.

Devolution

Resources for housing, job creation, social welfare, education and health are increasingly being channelled to the Maori people through tribal authorities and tribal organisations. Some of this funding would be used to provide services in Maori ways; some would be used to purchase services on the open market. Because of the variety of receiving organisations (some tribal, some not, some well-developed organisationally, others not) new definitions of accounta-bility are required to ensure that resources are being appropriately used and that there is an equitable distribution to the various Maori populations.

Biculturalism

Political and legal imperatives are forcing gradual recognition of political partnership for Maori. In the health services, a major issue is the provision of special services for Maori. In some instances, this has created public outrage, where Maori health services within gen-eral institutions have been shown to be unconventional or poorly managed. But there is no serious proposal that all Maori health needs should be provided in a separate system. So the present mono-cul-tural health service organisations must grapple with the definition of 'bicultural partnership', work to transform themselves and be pre-pared to support initiatives desired by the Maori people. A massive change in implicit and explicit social contracts between health ogani-

141

sations and the Maori people will be required. This could lead to new 'contracts' with the rest of the population.

In November 1988, the government released a policy statement: Partnership Response *Te Urupare Rangapu* (Appendix 2). A specific proposal is for the formation of an Iwi Transition Agency for a five year period, to help *iwi* to develop their operational base. This will now be a key local agency in the development of area health board policy for Maori participation in planning, advice and service provision. This reform introduces another potential organisational lag, but it is hoped that this will be minimised in the Waikato, due to the board's preparations and the vigorous efforts of *iwis* themselves.

Equal employment opportunities

The State Sector Act of 1988 which established general management in the health service includes specific reference to the responsibility of general managers to ensure recognition of 'the aims and aspirations of the Maori people; the employment requirements of the Maori people; and the need for greater involvement of the Maori people as employees of area health boards'.

While such requirements, and others in the act on equal employment opportunities, are laudable, they are impositions on the health service in the short term. Diversion of resources to support these new values must come from current commitments to health care, and the tapering-in of such mandated provisions without compromising the provision and quality of services will be a major exercise in itself.

The present economic environment is making equal employment opportunities an area of particular concern – not just in relation to Maori employment. Government funding of health boards was reduced by over 3 per cent in real terms in 1988/9 and cuts may be as much as 10 per cent in the next year. The national unemployment rate is running at 11 per cent and the less well educated and less skilled groups, particularly Maori, are greatly over-represented. The refocusing on care in the community is causing a reduction in unskilled jobs, such as kitchen and domestic assistants, cleaners and orderlies. All these occupations employ a large number of Maori, so despite efforts directed at employing a higher proportion of Maori in the health service, it is likely that, at least in the short term, the opposite will happen. The qualification of Maori to enter professional occupations and the restructuring of education and training to encourage such entry is now a high priority.

Purpose and intended values: internal

The Waikato Hospital Board's role and mission statement and the resulting guiding principles give recognition to certain values such as efficiency and equity:

> 'To provide in consultation with other agencies, appropriate inpatient, outpatient, day patient and extramural services which will promote a preventative, curative and caring service for the health of the people of the Waikato and its broader regional area, within the resources available to the Board.
>
> These services to be planned to ensure the maximum possible accessibility, quality and continuity of care, and efficiency in their provision.
>
> As far as possible, cognisance will also be taken of the need to liaise with other agencies to promote, develop, maintain and improve the health and well-being of the people within the Board's area, and to allow relevant public participation in the major decisions on the provision of Waikato Hospital Board services.'

These objectives give managers the opportunity to *allow* certain initiatives (in Maori health, for example); they can be referred to for *support*. But they do seem inadequate recognition of values that actively *promote* policy and service development for improving Maori health. There is cautious local political commitment to bicultural policies. Ironically, these developments have been slowed by the diversion of key Maori people to other issues, where biculturalism and Maori development are important, such as land, fishing and tribal issues.

Towards a better health result: key issues

In progressing towards a better health result, there are two key issues:

> promoting *social acceptability* for Maori partnership within the health services;

> establishing an organisation and *resource model* to support social acceptability.

Social acceptability

An essential aspect of quality of service is its acceptability to its users. Maori see this acceptability in two main areas:

provision of some services especially for Maori people and provided in Maori ways by Maori people;

services for the population at large which have been modified to be
sensitive to Maori values.

Satisfying Maori people is, in a way, the easier task for health service
managers, for the focus is clearer and the emotional change is for
gain, not loss. For the population at large, the change will also be all-
embracing, as all aspects of health services must become bicultural.
Calls for recognition of the Treaty of Waitangi, partnership and
Maori sovereignty are widely interpreted as based on avarice, a mis-
guided sense of history or afterthought. We can expect a 'white back-
lash' in health, as there has been in other sectors, and that this back-
lash will first be expressed by the providers and health professionals.

To anticipate such a reaction, a 'marketing plan' is proposed, with
three levels of consideration.

Level 1: social justice   At this level, acceptability is based on histori-
cal and social factors which justify partnership for Maori and the right
to choice and separate identity. Maori have a right to be healthy.

Level 2: unmet demand   If the health status of Maori could more
closely approach that of the rest of the population, the resources
saved could be applied to numerous unmet needs or wants.

Level 3: sickness focus   The Maori population has a poor level of
health, and this justifies special remedies.

At a policy level, the hospital board has established a standing Policy
Initiatives Committee, whose tasks are to develop policies on bicul-
turalism, quality assurance and client orientation. All these are
closely linked, but the desire to provide services in ways that satisfy
clients is of great significance. One aim of managers is that bicultural
policies be recognised as merely the expressed wishes of a sub-set of
clients.

Resource model

Within a block grant funding system with a population base, the basic
unit is a defined population. This is usually thought of as geographic,
but it could well be a population defined by tribal links.

The recognition of the different roles of funder and provider has
also aided the development of a resource model based on health service units (see Figure 12.1) which would then contract their services
from public, private or voluntary providers.

Figure 12.1   Resource model based on health service units

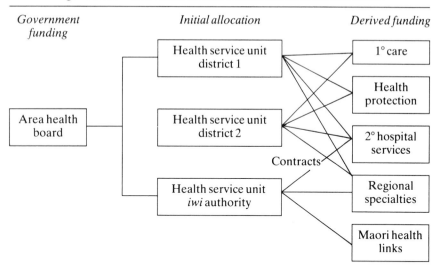

A major issue becomes one of enrolment or registration. Some Maori may opt not to 'enrol' with the *iwi* authority, preferring to remain within a district health service unit.

Major issues to be resolved would include the negotiation of contracts. *Iwi* authorities would have the opportunity to give Maori health initiatives first priority for funding. A corollary of that preference might be a restriction on the current high use of hospital services (about 60 per cent of psychiatric hospital patients are Maori). In the short term, therefore, services to some Maori individuals or groups might be compromised and reduced.

The overall level of funding, while population-related, would also have to be use- or need-based. Better definition and identification of Maori should enable the development of separate utilisation, mortality and fertility rates, which could then be applied as correcting, equity factors in funding models.

The most important advance in such a direct funding approach would be the immediate identification, at the time of contract setting, of the resources needed for and available to specific areas such as substance abuse, road accidents, smoking, accidents at home. This would make it possible to use uniquely Maori approaches to health promotion and the management of illness.

The lags caused by delayed area health board formation, local government reform and the restructuring of the Department of Maori Affairs have in turn delayed the conceptual development of relationships between funders and providers and, in particular, between health service units and services providers. But in the Waikato Area

Health Board, three geographical HSUs have been formed and are beginning to consider community consultation, service contracts, priority setting and resource allocation. The task of developing new relationships between funders and providers is not just a Maori issue; it is being faced by other equivalent organisations in the Waikato Area Health Board.

Current developments at the national level to establish a National Health Charter and contracts between the government and AHBs will bring support. These developments, together with the 'obligation set' between the Waikato AHB and its HSUs, and the HSU contracts with providers, should provide a new accountability pattern.

Conclusion

In our situation, managing for health result requires active political and social progress towards Maori partnership. The new level of managerial influence must be the tribe, the health of which, as a living organism, is as important as the health of any individual in it. The issues focus on process, but with the holistic nature of Maori health, the process of establishing and supporting Maori partnership is itself a health outcome.

A major environmental issue is the nature of the system within which managers manage for health result. Does a stable state called a health system exist? The processes described in this paper represent a disintegration and reintegration of relationships to focus on eventual health outcomes. Health managers could be seen as operating in an ever-changing environment where focus shifts from old and discarded to new and accepted factors which contribute, for that moment, to better health.

Appendix 1   The Treaty of Waitangi

English version

Article the first

The Chiefs of the Confederation of the United Tribes of New Zealand and the separate and independent Chiefs who have not become members of the Confederation cede to Her Majesty the Queen of England absolutely and without reservation all the rights and powers of Sovereignty which the said Confederation or Individual Chiefs respectively exercise or possess, or may be supposed to exercise or to possess over their respective Territories as the sole Sovereigns thereof.

Article the second

Her Majesty the Queen of England confirms and guarantees to the Chiefs and Tribes of New Zealand and to the respective families and individuals thereof the full exclusive and undisturbed possession of their Lands and Estates Forests Fisheries and other properties which they may collectively or individually possess so long as it is their wish and desire to retain the same in their possession; but the Chiefs of the United Tribes and the individual Chiefs yield to Her Majesty the exclusive rights of Preemption over such lands as the proprietors thereof may be disposed to alienate at such prices as may be agreed upon between the respective Proprietors and persons appointed by Her Majesty to treat with them in that behalf.

Article the third

In consideration thereof Her Majesty the Queen of England extends to the Natives of New Zealand Her royal protection and imparts to them all the Rights and Privileges of British Subjects.

Translation of Maori version (Professor H Kawharu)

The first

The Chiefs of the Confederation and all the Chiefs who have not joined that Confederation give absolutely to the Queen of England for ever the complete government over their land.

The second

The Queen of England agrees to protect the Chiefs, the Subtribes and all the people of New Zealand in the unqualified exercise of their chieftainship over their lands, villages and all their treasures. But on the other hand the Chiefs of the Confederation and all the Chiefs will sell land to the Queen at a price agreed to by the person owning it and by the person buying it (the latter being) appointed by the Queen as her purchase agent.

The third

For this agreed arrangement therefore concerning the Government of the Queen, the Queen of England will protect all the ordinary people of New Zealand and will give them the same rights and duties of citizenship as the people of England.

From: The Treaty of Waitangi and Social Policy, Discussion Booklet No 1. The Royal Commission on Social Policy, July 1987.

Appendix 2   Reaffirming the Government's objectives

The Government reaffirms the principle objectives set out in *He Tirohanga Rangapu*. These are to:

- honour the principles of the Treaty of Waitangi through exercising its powers of government reasonably, and in good faith, so as to actively protect the Maori interests specified in the Treaty

- eliminate the gaps which exist between the educational, personal, social, economic and cultural well-being of Maori people and that of the general population, that disadvantage Maori people, and that do not result from individual or cultural preferences

- provide opportunities for Maori people to develop economic activities as a sound base for realising their aspirations, and in order to promote self-sufficiency and eliminate attitudes of dependency

- deal fairly, justly and expeditiously with breaches of the Treaty of Waitangi and the grievances between the Crown and Maori people which arise out of them

- provide for the Maori language and culture to receive an equitable allocation of resources and a fair opportunity to develop, having regard to the contribution being made by Maori language and culture toward the development of a unique New Zealand identity

- promote decision making in the machinery of government, in areas of importance to Maori communities, which provide opportunities for Maori people to actively participate, on jointly agreed terms, in such policy formulation and service delivery

- encourage Maori participation in the political process.

From: Partnership Response, Policy Statement. Office of the Minister of Maori Affairs, November 1988.

REFLECTIONS

Nan Carle

The King's Fund International Seminar is above all a time when a selected group of managers and policy makers come together to explore how to learn from each other's experience. This assumes that many problems facing individuals are not parochial, that 'in all problems exist all problems'. We see this philosophical tenet acted out many times in the case studies presented in this volume. There are local trends which have similar features across the western world, and thus everyone has something to offer to the solution and everyone has something to gain from the experience of others.

Such coming together also assumes that people have a considerable capacity to listen. As an observer, I felt that there was a concentrated effort to listen at the seminar – even though the language barrier between English-speaking people was at times very considerable. Words such as 'competition', 'choice', 'market', 'incentives' and 'regulation' were each interpreted very differently, according to individual environment and experience. Sometimes such discomfort can lead to greater learning, and I believe that to have been so during the seminar.

Nowhere during the week was discomfort more unmasked than with the notion that some managers were preoccupied with 'doing things right' to the exclusion of adequate concern about whether they were 'doing the right things'. There was a dangerous potential for participants to sling mud along with such sentiments as 'I care more than you do' versus 'but I achieve results'. Fortunately, this negative potential was not realised. People listened and clarified. There was at times, however, a restless unease. The tension is clear if we compare the papers I classified as primarily concerned with relevance to need or equity and social acceptability with the papers I plotted as primarily concerned with efficiency and economy.

Efforts to bring doctors and clinicians into management have been plotted in the quality dimension of efficiency and economy. The inclusion of doctors in management has been an important response to the cost limiting exercises that characterised the latter half of the 1980s. At times during the seminar, however, there seemed to be an assumption that involving doctors in management would of itself ensure that organisations were safeguarding quality of care. It seemed to suit both clinicians and managers to assume this to be the case without putting into place rigorous methods for evaluating the impact of interventions on the quality dimension of efficiency and economy, or any of the other five dimensions in Maxwell's definition. This assumption did not go entirely unchallenged. The participants agreed that the next seminar should oversee their progress in developing management systems that safeguarded quality and kept open the discussion of the roles and responsibilities of both doctors and managers.

The seminar heard some very different perspectives on relevance to need. Cameron Waddell's paper, about working with a group of employers from a particular company, showed that, for him, 'relevance' of health result was linked to what was relevant to the company. Brendon Kearney was concerned particularly with the clinical considerations of managing resources to best serve people with cancer. Alasdair Liddell's case study of 'health for all' was about thinking through long-term health issues for an inner city population. At this point, discomfort grew: how to be 'relevant' and 'doing the right thing' while managing to ensure results *now*? Managers measured results on different time-scales: some looked to the immediate present while others looked much further into the future.

In unravelling the debate about short-term versus long-term solutions it was not possible to make an easy distinction between those from 'private' health care institutions and those from a national health care system. The American examples put forward by Robert Johnson and Scott Parker had many of the same features as those put forward by Alasdair Liddell in Britain or Glenn Garlick in New Zealand. In general terms, though, the Americans operated in an environment where there were no guarantees for their survival. For them 'doing things right' in the short term was a necessary tactic in enabling them to continue to provide a service at all. They faced economic threats that were clear and immediate. Those from a more regulated state controlled system had a different set of threats. They were not so hampered by immediate economic threats to their survival. Health as a matter of right not wealth gave them a different set of experiences in prioritising and targeting resources to specific client groups. They have a social mandate to be 'all things to all people' but the finite resources mean that public decisions have to be made about choices. These were not easy to make with a clear understanding of their impact on either the short-term or long-term delivery of health care. How to manage the flow of resources was essential to all parties regardless of the economic environment they worked in. 'In all problems exist all problems.'

Managers of such high calibre knew they could solve problems. Their struggle during the seminar was whether or not they were facing the right problems. There was an agreed difference of defining health result according to who would be judging the result and at what level. Four different judges emerged:

If it is 'society' then the result is 'health for all'.

If it is the 'community' then the result is 'health status'.

If it is the 'individual' then the result is 'capacity for cure'.

If it is the 'organisation' then the result is 'financial and structural'.

These judges gave each of the participants an insight into how they were approaching the problem.

Another insight into sharing the learning between participants of different backgrounds came from a systems diagram offered by Gordon Best, Director of the King's Fund College. He was particularly concerned to get past the cut and dry dichotomy of 'doing things right' versus 'doing the right things' by considering three variables.

What business are you in – prevention or caring and repair?

How do you operate – policy or service?

Whom do you serve – some people or all people?

The chart (Figure 13.1) was presented with a request to managers to plot their own organisations.

Figure 13.1

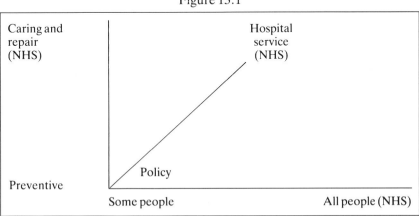

After completing the chart managers were encouraged to decide whether they wanted to make fundamental changes in the nature of their organisations or whether they wanted to manage differently within the existing environment. Both decisions meant managing change but at different levels.

From the week, I took three sets of challenges for managers interested in managing for health result into the 1990s and beyond. The first, which is unique to health care and which makes managing health services different from managing a business like selling cars, is the tradition surrounding the Hippocratic oath. Both Robert Maxwell and Cyril Chantler talked about the tension doctors feel in treating individual patients as best they can while being part of an organisation that has real financial constraints. The organisation cannot be all things to all people. How doctors are involved in setting priorities and allocating resources to some people and not others will make a significant difference to us all, whether we are involved in the provision of health care or in receiving it.

Rather than reconsidering the Hippocractic oath as is suggested by some I would prefer that we find new ways of looking at the problem of serving the individual in the face of finite resources. At the moment both doctors and managers keep the patient/client distant from their own health care. A new interactive relationship may empower all parties to 'do more with less' while increasing the self reliance of each other.

In Britain, as in other countries, there is a drive to separate the purchasing and providing functions so that health care can be more efficiently and effectively delivered. Figure 13.2 indicates the three sets of relationships which need managing for high quality health result.

What I took away from the international seminar was the belief that the third party – the service user – also needs to have a new set of roles and responsibilities in such a division of labour. Otherwise no

Figure 13.2

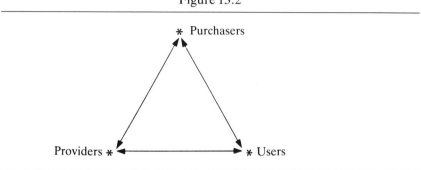

one would be empowered to improve health result. Therefore the first set of challenges for managers facing the 'right problems' is to reform the way in which they interact with their consumers and the resources consumers bring with them to the solution of finite finances.

Once managers have considered the nature of their business and their partnerships in it the second set of challenges is about management logistics. Making sure that scarce resources are wisely and efficiently spent is a crucial dimension of quality. There is at present, however, the potential for managers to overemphasise efficiency and economy at the expense of the other dimensions of access, equity, effectiveness and social acceptability. Even so, current management systems cannot adequately assess the impact of management effort according to any dimensions of quality. In these studies the act of evaluation ranged from an unspoken assumption that involving doctors in management would help to ensure quality to the appointment of a director of evaluation to change the culture. The systems available seem to be neither quick enough nor relevant enough to help managers make informed decisions. How and *what* to measure needs a great deal more exploration between managers, doctors and all parties so that we are the masters not the victims of change.

In this final chapter I have tried to present some of the key themes from the week and also to put forward my own thoughts as to what challenges lie ahead. My challenges are based on the notion that we could be involved in an international paradigm shift away from a model of management that has operational answers to specific problems – away from a curative style of health care towards a model of management that seeks a negotiated order and uses the resources of all parties creatively – towards a health care system where variety is increased and power is dispersed.

Then we will have an organisation of health care where there is negotiated order through more balanced power which allows for constant and adaptive change.

MANAGING FOR HEALTH RESULT:
KING'S FUND INTERNATIONAL SEMINAR 1988
LIST OF PARTICIPANTS

J S Bradbrook, District General Manager, Wigan
Health Authority   *UK*

Cyril Chantler, Chairman, Management Board,
Guy's Acute Unit, Guy's Hospital (now Clinical
Dean, United Medical and Dental Schools of Guy's
and St Thomas's Hospitals)   *UK*

Lucy Dobbin (National Coordinator), Executive
Director, Health Sciences Centre, Newfoundland   *Canada*

Tom Frawley, General Manager, Western Health
and Social Services Board, Londonderry   *UK*

Glenn Garlick, Chief Executive, Waikato Hospital
Board (now General Manager, Waikato Area Health
Board)   *New Zealand*

Christine Hancock, General Manager, Waltham
Forest Health Authority (now General Secretary,
Royal College of Nursing)   *UK*

Stephen W Herbert, President, Royal Victoria
Hospital, Montreal   *Canada*

Robert Johnson, Chief Executive Officer, St Louis
Regional Medical Center (now Executive Director,
Grady Memorial Hospital, Atlanta)   *USA*

Brendon Kearney, Administrator, Royal Adelaide
Hospital   *Australia*

David Kenny, Regional General Manager, North
West Thames Regional Health Authority   *UK*

David King (National Coordinator), formerly
District General Manager, Exeter Health Authority   *UK*

Richard Knapp, Senior Vice President, Association
of American Medical Colleges, Washington DC   *USA*

David Knowles, General Manager, Riverside Health Authority — *UK*

Dieter Kuntz, Executive Director, Victoria General Hospital, Winnipeg — *Canada*

Stephen Leeder, Department of Community and Geriatric Medicine, University of Sydney (now Director, Department of Community Medicine, University of Sydney) — *Australia*

Alasdair Liddell, District General Manager, Bloomsbury Health Authority (now Chief Executive, East Anglian Regional Health Authority) — *UK*

Bernie McKay, Bernie McKay and Associates, Wanniassa — *Australia*

Sandy MacPherson, Medical Officer of Health, Department of Public Health, Toronto — *Canada*

Robert J Maxwell, Secretary and Chief Executive Officer, King Edward's Hospital Fund for London — *UK*

John Morris, Executive Director, Australian Hospital Association (now Chief Executive Officer, Peter MacCallum Cancer Institute, Melbourne) — *Australia*

Jon Mulligan (National Coordinator), Director of Medical Services, Sir Charles Gairdner Hospital, Nedlands — *Australia*

Richard A Norling, Executive Vice President, LHS Corporation, Los Angeles (now President, Fairview Hospital and Healthcare Services, Minneapolis) — *USA*

Scott S Parker, President, Intermountain Health Care Incorporated, Salt Lake City — *USA*

George Salmond, Director-General, Department of Health, Wellington — *New Zealand*

C Thomas Smith, President, Yale–New Haven Hospital, New Haven — *USA*

J Douglas Snedden, Education Director, Hospital for Sick Children, Etobicoke — *Canada*

Cameron Waddell, Manager, Occupational Health, Petro-Canada Incorporated, Calgary — *Canada*